PRACTICAL OSCILLOSCOPE HANDBOOK

Volumes 1 & 2

RUFUS P. TURNER

PRACTICAL
OSCILLOSCOPE
HANDBOOK

Volume 1

RUFUS P. TURNER

JOHN F. RIDER PUBLISHER, INC., NEW YORK

a division of HAYDEN PUBLISHING COMPANY, INC.

Preface to Volume 1

The *PRACTICAL OSCILLOSCOPE HANDBOOK* (in two volumes) has been written for technicians and others who want to know in a few words how to use the oscilloscope in a variety of test situations. It assumes that its users are already grounded in electronic fundamentals and, therefore, does not present general theory or measurements theory. Its readers will find it to be a highly useful guide for oscilloscope manipulation and interpretation of oscilloscope display. The directions are as succinct and recipe-like as is possible and theory has been avoided except where a digest is essential for understanding the application.

The reader who has very little familiarity with the operating principles, structure, and characteristics of the oscilloscope will find a simplified presentation of these details in the first three chapters. The author has tried to avoid an over-use of technical jargon and uses skeleton circuits and block diagrams instead of hopelessly detailed full circuits in his explanations in these chapters. The reader who already has control over this information may skip Chapters 1, 2, and 3.

The final seven chapters of this volume give step-by-step directions for tests and measurements in the areas identified by the chapter titles. These include tests of a general nature (current, voltage, frequency, phase) and specialized applications (amplifier, receiver, and transmitter testing) of interest to laboratory technicians, students, service technicians, radio amateurs, and electronic hobbyists. Any of the tests may be made with a relatively simple oscilloscope. (Volume 2 covers industrial and scientific applications.)

Some screening of material has been unavoidable. In the last twenty years oscilloscope applications have accumulated at such a pace that a good-sized set of books would be needed to contain them all. A conscientious effort, therefore, was made to include here only those instructions for which there seems to be the greatest call, and above all to exclude laboratory curiosities. The reader will certainly find serviceable information in this book. For a more detailed treatment of instruments and applications, the reader is referred to the *Encyclopedia on Cathode-Ray Oscilloscopes and Their Uses* by J. F. Rider and S. D. Uslan, published by J. F. Rider Publishers, Inc., New York City.

Altadena, California   RUFUS P. TURNER
February 1964

Table of Contents

SAFETY NOTICE

Every oscilloscope contains high voltages which can electrocute you. Be extraordinarily careful when you work inside this instrument. Never work inside a live oscilloscope or operate it with its cover removed unless you are thoroughly familiar with the instrument circuit and take care to avoid touching any high-voltage point. The oscilloscope is dangerously deceptive; it has high voltage in many unexpected places.

In most oscilloscopes, as in other test instruments, the metal outer case is connected internally to the GROUND or COMMON input terminal. When this terminal is connected to a high-voltage point in a circuit under test, the entire case becomes dangerous to touch. Be alert when you *must* use the instrument in this manner.

Follow every electrical safety rule (keep one hand in your pocket, insulate yourself from ground, use insulated tools and/or rubber gloves, know the circuit you test, connect the instrument before you apply test-circuit voltage, etc.).

The cathode-ray tube is highly evacuated. If broken, it can scatter glass fragments at high speed, possibly inflicting grievous wounds. Handle this tube with care and avoid striking, scratching, or dropping it.

Chapter 1

First Principles

Of all electronic test instruments, the oscilloscope comes closest to being indispensable. So versatile is this device that if a technician were limited to a single instrument, his choice of an oscilloscope would, in the majority of cases, be the wisest. The oscilloscope can show a great many things about the behavior of circuits and the nature of currents and voltages in them.

This chapter explains the oscilloscope in what we hope is the least technical language. It is written for newcomers who have little or no knowledge of the subject, and for old hands who need a simple brushup. (You can safely skip it if you already are expert in fundamentals.) Without apology, it uses analogies, where possible, in the belief that new facts often are clearer to the reader when they are compared with familiar old ones.

1.1 WHAT THE OSCILLOSCOPE IS

Basically the oscilloscope is an electron-beam voltmeter. Its indications are produced by applied signal voltages that deflect a thin beam of electrons instead of a pointer. Since it has no significant weight, the electron beam can move several million times faster than the lightest pointer. Completely free of mechanical parts, the oscilloscope is a true electronic instrument.

In its performance, however, the oscilloscope is unlike any other voltmeter. The electron beam faithfully follows rapid variations in signal voltage and traces a visible path on a screen. In this way, rapid alternations, pulsations, or transients are reproduced and the operator can see their waveform, as well as measure their amplitude. Because of its completely electronic nature, the oscilloscope can reproduce high-frequency waves which are much too fast for such electromechanical devices as direct-writing recorders and oscillographs.

Before the oscilloscope was developed, a technician could not "see" a high-frequency waveform but had to piece together a graph of it from data laboriously taken, point by point. And even then, phase relations and distortion (immediately evident on an oscilloscope screen) had to be painstakingly calculated. But the oscilloscope has removed the "uncertainty of the unseen" and has simplified many tests and measurements. In doing so, it has become an immensely useful tool in the electronics laboratory, repair shop, radio station, and classroom. This instrument is also invaluable in any field where a phenomenon may be converted into a proportional voltage for observation—meteorology, medicine, biology, chemistry, mathematics, psychology, etc.

The oscilloscope, then, is a kind of voltmeter which uses an electron beam instead of a pointer, and a kind of recorder which uses

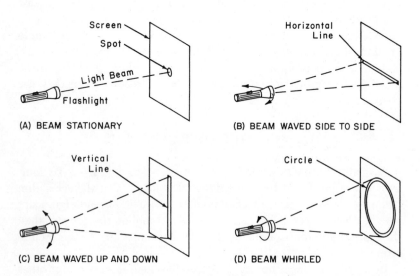

FIG. 1-1. The light-beam analogy.

an electron beam instead of a pen. It saves test time by directly displaying a phenomenon.

1.2 THE ELECTRON BEAM

The action of a beam of light illustrates how the electron beam works in an oscilloscope.

Point a sharply focused flashlight at a screen or wall, as in Fig. 1-1A, and the light beam will make a bright dot where it strikes the screen. Hold the flashlight still and the dot remains stationary; move it and the dot is displaced on the screen. If the movement is slow, the eye can easily follow the spot. But if the movement, always along the same line, is too fast for the eye to follow, as happens when the flashlight is waved rapidly, *persistence of vision* causes the eye to see the pattern traced by the spot. Thus, wave the flashlight from side to side to trace a horizontal line (Fig. 1-1B) and up and down for a vertical line (Fig. 1-1C), or whirl it for a circle (Fig. 1-1D). If the hand were steady and fast enough, the light beam could be used in this way for any kind of writing or drawing.

A similar action takes place in the cathode-ray tube (CRT) of an oscilloscope. The flashlight is replaced by an *electron gun,* the light beam by a narrow *electron beam,* and the external screen by the flat end of the glass tube, which is chemically coated to form a fluorescent *screen.* Figure 1-2 shows this arrangement. Here, the electron gun generates the beam which moves down the tube and strikes the screen. The screen glows (fluoresces) at the point of collision, producing a bright dot. When the beam is deflected, by

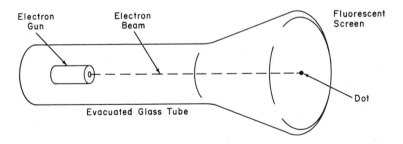

FIG. 1-2. The basic structure of the cathode-ray tube.

means of an electric or magnetic field, the dot will move accordingly to trace out a pattern.

The electron gun contains several parts arranged in this sequence:

1. A heated *cathode* out of which the beam electrons are boiled.
2. A *control electrode,* powered by a negative d-c voltage, which regulates brightness of the trace.
3. A first *accelerating electrode,* powered by a positive d-c voltage, which speeds up the beam.
4. A *focusing electrode,* powered by a positive d-c voltage, which narrows the beam to give a thin, sharp trace.
5. A second *accelerating electrode,* powered by a positive d-c voltage, which speeds up the beam.

After leaving the cathode, electrons pass through a tiny hole in each of the electrodes before they reach the screen. As you can see, the electron gun is both the source of the electron beam and an electronic system that controls the beam's focus and brightness.

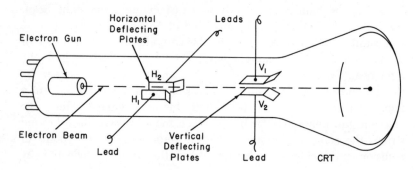

FIG. 1-3. The arrangement of the deflecting plates.

1.3 HOW THE BEAM IS DEFLECTED

The electron beam may be deflected transversely by means of an electric field *(electrostatic deflection)* or a magnetic field *(electromagnetic deflection).* Most oscilloscopes use electrostatic deflection, as it permits higher-frequency operation and requires negligible power. Electromagnetic deflection is common in TV picture tubes.

The principles of electrostatic deflection are rudimentary. Because electrons are negatively charged particles, they are attracted by a positive charge or field and repelled by a negative one. Since the electron beam is a stream of electrons, a positive field will divert it in one direction, and a negative field will divert it in an opposite direction. To move the beam in this way in the CRT, *deflecting plates* are mounted inside the tube, as shown in Fig. 1-3, and suitable deflecting voltages are applied to them.

These plates are arranged in two pairs: H_1 and H_2 for deflecting the beam horizontally, and V_1 and V_2 for deflecting it vertically. Leads are attached for external connections. The beam passes down the tube between the four plates. When the plates are at zero voltage, the beam is midway between them, and the spot is in the center of the screen (Fig. 1-4A). When H_1 is made positive with respect to the cathode (all other plates at zero voltage), it attracts the beam, and the spot moves horizontally to the left (Fig. 1-4B); when H_2 is made positive, the beam is attracted toward that plate, and the spot moves horizontally to the right (Fig. 1-4C). Similarly, when V_1 is made positive, it attracts the beam, and the spot moves vertically upward (Fig. 1-4D); when V_2 is made positive, the beam is attracted toward that plate, and the spot moves vertically downward (Fig. 1-4E). In each of these deflections, the displacement of the beam (and therefore the distance traveled by the spot) is proportional to the voltage applied to the plate.

If a negative voltage is applied to any plate, the beam will be repelled, rather than attracted, and the deflection will be in a direction opposite to that indicated in the preceding paragraph. Thus, when V_2 is made negative, it will repel the beam, and the spot will move vertically upward.

As was mentioned in Section 1.2, when a spot moves too rapidly for the eye to follow, it traces a line. This is what happens in the CRT when a rapidly pulsating or alternating voltage is applied to the deflecting plates; the beam is flipped back and forth so rapidly that the spot traces a line. When a positive pulsating voltage is applied to H_1 (or a negative pulsating voltage to H_2), the spot traces a horizontal line from center to left (Fig. 1-4F); when the positive pulsating voltage is applied to H_2 (or negative pulsating voltage to H_1), the spot traces a horizontal line from center to right

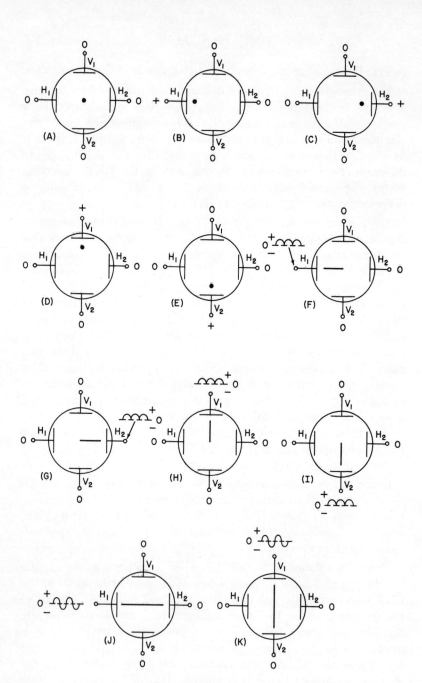

FIG. 1-4. Deflection when the voltage is applied
to one axis.

(Fig. 1-4G). Similarly, when the positive pulsating voltage is applied to V_1 (or negative pulsating voltage to V_2), the spot traces a vertical line from center upward (Fig. 1-4H); when the positive pulsating voltage is applied to V_2 (or negative pulsating voltage to V_1), the spot traces a vertical line downward (Fig. 1-4I).

When an alternating deflection voltage is applied to H_1 or H_2, the spot moves alternately from center to one side and back, and from center to the opposite side and back—tracing a line that passes through the center of the screen. (This results from the alternate attraction and repulsion of the beam by the positive and negative a-c half-cycles.) Thus, a horizontal line is traced when an a-c voltage is applied to either horizontal plate (Fig. 1-4J); a vertical line is traced when an a-c voltage is applied to either vertical plate (Fig. 1-4K).

All of these examples show what happens when a voltage is applied to the horizontal *or* vertical deflecting plates. When a horizontal and a vertical voltage are applied simultaneously, deflection of the beam is proportional to the resultant of the two voltages, and the position of the spot is intermediate between the horizontal and vertical axes of the screen. This is illustrated by the patterns in Fig. 1-5.

In Fig. 1-5A-D, a steady positive voltage is applied to one horizontal plate and one vertical plate. When these two deflecting voltages are equal, the position of the spot is 45° from the horizontal axis, as shown. The angle is proportionately greater than 45° (spot closer to vertical axis) when the vertical voltage is the higher of the two, and is less than 45° (spot closer to horizontal axis) when the horizontal voltage is the higher. When two negative voltages are used, deflection is in the opposite direction.

If, instead of a steady voltage, a pulsating positive voltage is applied to the same plates as in the preceding example, the patterns in Fig. 1-5E-H will be obtained. Here, as before, the tilt of the trace is 45° from horizontal when the two voltages are equal and in phase. The tilt is greater than 45° (outer tip closer to vertical axis) when the vertical voltage is the higher of the two, and is less than 45° (outer tip closer to horizontal axis) when the horizontal voltage is the higher. When a negative pulsating voltage is applied to both plates, the trace extends in the opposite direction.

When an alternating voltage is applied to the plates *in phase*, the patterns of Fig. 1-5I-J are obtained. As in the preceding example,

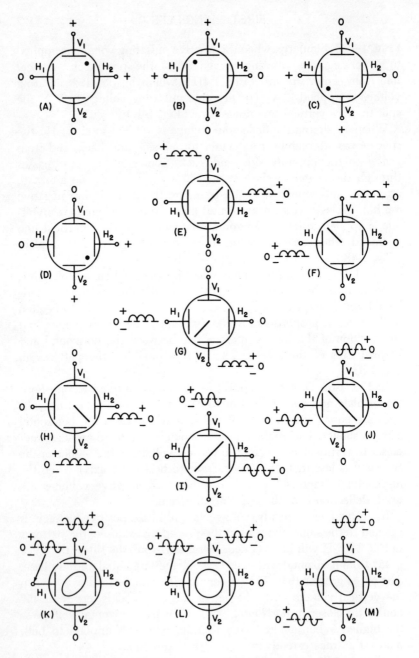

FIG. 1-5. Deflection when the voltage is applied
to both axes.

the tilt of the trace is 45° from the horizontal when the two voltages are equal. The tilt is greater than 45° (tips closer to vertical axis) when the vertical voltage is the higher of the two, and is less than 45° (tips closer to horizontal axis) when the horizontal voltage is the higher. Actually, two more patterns (the a-c equivalent of Fig. 1-5G and H) are obtained when a-c voltages are applied to H_1 and V_2, and H_2 and V_2, respectively, but to the eye these patterns are the same as those of Fig. 1-5I and J. The a-c trace has the same length from center-screen to each tip when the ac is symmetrical; when the ac is asymmetrical, the shorter half of the trace corresponds to the lower-voltage half-cycle.

A single-line trace is obtained only when the phase angle between the horizontal and vertical a-c voltages is 0°, 180°, or 360°. At other phase angles, a double-line trace is obtained: at equal voltages the pattern becomes an ellipse with right tilt (Fig. 1-5K) for angles between 0° and 90°; a circle at 90° (Fig. 1-5L); an ellipse with left tilt (Fig. 1-5M) between 90° and 180°; again an ellipse with left tilt between 180° and 270°; again a circle at 270°; and again an ellipse with left tilt between 270° and 360°. At 0° and 360°, the single line tilts right (Fig. 1-5I); at 180°, it tilts left (Fig. 1-5J).

1.4 CRT FEATURES

Electrostatic cathode-ray tubes are available in a number of types and sizes to suit individual instrument requirements. A brief discussion of the important features of these tubes follows. Detailed electrical and mechanical data may be found in tube manufacturers' tables.

Size. Size refers to screen diameter. CRT's are available in 1-, 2-, 3-, 5-, and 7-inch sizes for oscilloscope use. The 5-inch size is the most common for stationary and general-purpose oscilloscopes; the 3-inch size is the most common for portable instruments. The first figure in the type number usually expresses the size. Thus, the 5GP1 is a 5-inch tube.

Phosphor. The screen is coated with a fluorescent chemical called a *phosphor*. This material determines the color and persistence of the trace, and the phosphor number indicates both. The trace colors in electrostatic CRT's for oscilloscope use are blue, blue-green, and green (white is used for television; blue-white, orange, and yellow are used for radar). Persistence in these tubes is expressed as *short, medium,* and *long;* this refers to the length of time the trace remains on the screen after the signal has ended.

The phosphors of oscilloscope tubes are designated as follows: P1, green medium; P2, blue-green medium; P5, blue very short; and P11, blue short. These designations are combined in the tube type number. Thus, the 5GP1 is a 5-inch tube with a medium-persistence green trace.

Medium persistence trace suits most general-purpose applications. Long persistence is needed for transient studies, since it keeps the image on the screen for observation for a short period after the fast transient has disappeared. This persistence is invaluable, also, for displaying very slow phenomena which otherwise would only produce a slow-moving dot on the screen. Short persistence is needed for extremely high-speed phenomena, to prevent the smearing and interference caused when one image persists into the period of the next one. Phosphor P11 is considered to be the best for photographing from the CRT screen.

Operating Voltages. The CRT requires a heater voltage (commonly 6.3 v ac or dc at 600 ma, but 2.5 v at 2.1 amp in a few types) and several d-c voltages which depend upon tube type. The latter include:

1. Negative grid (control electrode) voltage, −14 to −200 v.
2. Positive anode no. 1 (focusing electrode) voltage, 100-1100 v.
3. Positive anode no. 2 (accelerating electrode) voltage, 600-6000 v.
4. Positive anode no. 3 (accelerating electrode in some types) voltage, 200-20,000 v.

Deflection Voltages. Either an a-c or d-c voltage will deflect the beam (see Section 1.3). The distance through which the spot moves on the screen is proportional to the d-c or peak a-c amplitude.

The deflection sensitivity of the tube usually is stated as the d-c voltage (or peak a-c voltage) required for each inch of deflection of the spot on the screen. (Sometimes this is given in rms volts, and sometimes in centimeters deflection.) Sensitivity is stated separately for the horizontal and vertical plates. It varies between 26 and 310 dcv/in. for horizontal, and between 18 and 350 dcv/in. for vertical, depending upon tube type.

Complex Tubes. Some oscilloscope CRT's have more than one electron gun. This permits the simultaneous display of signals on the single screen. Such tubes are available with two to four guns but are not common. Operating and deflecting voltages are applied separately to each gun; each one has separate controls for focus, brightness, and other adjustments.

1.5 VIEWING SCREENS

It is hard to denote the exact position of the spot on the plain face of the CRT. A properly graduated transparent screen, therefore, is placed in front of the tube for accurate measurement and observation of spot position.

Such screens (known variously by the terms *graticule, grating, grid, grid screen, mask,* and *screen*) take several familiar forms. The principal ones are shown in Fig. 1-6. The major divisions on these screens usually are either centimeters or half-inches. Some screens, especially those intended for radio and television servicing, have markers to indicate a calibrating-voltage deflection, such as 1 v peak-to-peak.

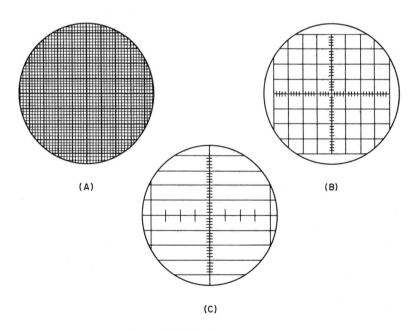

(A)   (B)   (C)

FIG. 1-6. Viewing screens.

1.6 FUNCTION OF AMPLIFIERS

Some of the voltages listed under *Deflection Voltages* in Section 1.4 are high. A CRT vertical sensitivity of 50 dcv/in., for example, means that 150 volts dc or peak ac will be needed to move the spot three inches on the screen. Such a strong signal is seldom available, so weak ones must be raised to this level. Deflection amplifiers are used for this purpose in an oscilloscope.

An oscilloscope has separate horizontal and vertical amplifiers. The frequency response of these amplifiers must be wide enough to accommodate faithfully the entire band of frequencies handled by the oscilloscope. The passband of a high-quality laboratory instrument extends from dc to a frequency of 30 to 1000 mc; a less costly television service oscilloscope must have a 5-mc passband. An oscilloscope intended for audio testing usually handles ac only and has an upper limit of 200 kc. The sensitivity (gain) of oscilloscope amplifiers affords deflection of 20 to 200 mv/in. in low-cost instruments, and 0.5 mv/in. or better in high-priced ones.

Most oscilloscopes provide direct access to the deflection plates, so that a high-voltage signal, when available, may be applied to the plates without unnecessarily going through an amplifier.

1.7 FUNCTION OF SWEEP GENERATOR

The amplitude of a voltage may be directly measured on a calibrated viewing screen from the length of the straight-line trace it produces (Fig. 1-4F-K). This is entirely satisfactory for a d-c voltage, but the straight line tells little or nothing about the waveform of an a-c voltage, pulsating voltage, or transient. What is needed is a graph of the voltage, traced on the screen by the spot.

To obtain such a display, the signal voltage is applied to the vertical plates (directly or through the vertical amplifier) and it moves the spot vertically to positions corresponding to the instantaneous values of the signal. At the same time, the spot is deflected horizontally across the screen by a *sweep voltage* applied to the horizontal plates. The combined action of these two voltages causes the spot to trace out the signal: the horizontal sweep voltage provides the time base by moving the spot horizontally with time, while the signal voltage moves the spot vertically in proportion to the voltage at a particular instant in time.

There are two important sweep-generator requirements: (1) The sweep must be linear—the sweep voltage must rise linearly to the maximum value required for full-screen horizontal deflection of the spot. (2) The spot must always be swept in one direction (normally, left to right) but not in the "return" direction (right to left)—if this is not done, the signal will be traced backwards during the return sweep. This means that the sweep voltage must drop suddenly after reaching its maximum value. These requirements call for a sweep voltage having a linear sawtooth waveform (see Fig. 1-7A).

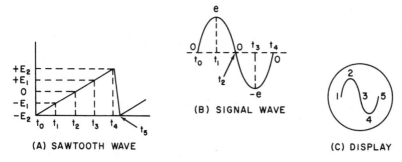

(A) SAWTOOTH WAVE

(B) SIGNAL WAVE

(C) DISPLAY

FIG. 1-7. Details of the sawtooth sweep.

The manner in which this sawtooth sweep operates is indicated in Fig. 1-7A-C. At time t_0, the sawtooth voltage is $-E_2$; this negative horizontal voltage moves the spot to point 1 on the screen (Fig. 1-7C). At this instant, the signal voltage is zero (t_0 in Fig. 1-7B), so the spot rests at the left end of the zero line of the screen. At time t_1, the linearly increasing sawtooth reaches $-E_1$, which, being more positive, moves the spot to screen point 2. At this instant, the signal voltage is e, the positive peak value, so point 2 is the maximum upward deflection of the spot. At time t_2, the sawtooth voltage is zero, there is no horizontal deflection, and the spot is at center screen (point 3). At this instant, the signal voltage is zero, so there is no vertical deflection either. At time t_3, the sawtooth voltage is $+E_1$, moving the spot to point 4. At this instant, the signal is $-e$, the negative peak value, so point 4 is the maximum downward deflection of the spot. At time t_4, the sawtooth voltage is $+E_2$, moving the spot to point 5. At this instant, the signal voltage is zero, so the spot is not vertically deflected. Between t_4 and t_5, the sawtooth voltage quickly falls through zero to its initial value of $-E_2$, snapping the spot back to position 1 in time to sweep forward on the next cycle of signal voltage.

When sweep and signal frequency are equal, a single cycle appears on the screen; when sweep is lower than signal, several cycles appear (in the ratio of the two frequencies); when sweep is higher than signal, less than one cycle appears. The display is stationary only when the two frequencies are either equal or in integral multiple relationship. At other frequencies, the display will drift horizontally.

Sawtooth sweep voltage is generated by a multivibrator, relaxation oscillator, or pulse generator. The upper frequency generated by internal devices in the oscilloscope is 50 to 100 kc in audio instruments, 500 to 1000 kc in television service instruments, and up to several megacycles in high-quality laboratory instruments. In some oscilloscopes, the sweep is calibrated in cps and kc; in others it is calibrated in time units (microseconds, milliseconds, and seconds).

Recurrent Sweep. When the sawtooth, being an a-c voltage, rapidly alternates, the display is repetitively presented, so that the eye sees a lasting pattern. This repeated operation is termed *recurrent sweep.*

Single Sweep. The opposite of recurrent sweep is single sweep. The latter produces one sweep of the spot across the screen in response to a trigger signal which may be initiated by the signal under study or by means of a switch.

Driven Sweep. The sweep generator is said to be free-running when it operates independently. A hazard of this type of operation, in some applications, is the chance that the sweep cycle will start *after* the signal cycle, thereby missing a part of the signal. Driven sweep removes this possibility because it is initiated by the signal; the signal cycle and sweep cycle therefore start in step. Both driven single sweep and driven recurrent sweep are available.

Non-sawtooth Sweep. In some applications, especially where waveform is of no interest, linear sweep is not needed. In such instances, sine waves or other shapes may be used for sweeping. The patterns in Fig. 1-5K-M, for example, are produced when a sine-wave sweep is used with a sine-wave signal of the same frequency.

1.8 SYNCHRONIZATION

Sweep frequency drift causes an unsteady pattern; this is seen in pattern migration across the screen and in a change in the number of cycles displayed.

Drift is eliminated by synchronizing the sweep generator with another frequency source (external sync) or with the signal itself (internal sync). The generator may be synchronized from either the positive or negative half-cycle of sync voltage, which are usually selected with a switch on the front panel of the oscilloscope. Sync voltage is injected at a suitable point in the sweep generator circuit.

1.9 BLANKING

During the brief *flyback* interval (t_4 to t_5 in Fig. 1-7A), when the sweep voltage snaps from its final amplitude back to its initial value, the spot backtracks across the screen to the starting point. This action can trace an extraneous line (the *retrace*) across the display, as shown from B to A in Fig. 1-8A.

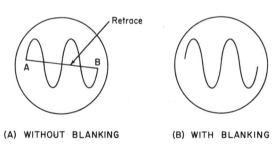

(A) WITHOUT BLANKING   (B) WITH BLANKING

FIG. 1-8. The effect of retrace blanking.

The retrace inserts a false line in the pattern, which causes confusion and inaccuracy. In modern oscilloscopes, the retrace is eliminated by darkening the screen during the flyback; the beam is cut off during this interval. This is done by momentarily applying a negative cutoff voltage (generated by the flyback) to the control electrode. Figure 1-8A shows the pattern defaced by the retrace; Fig. 1-8B shows the pattern with blanking.

1.10 INTENSITY MODULATION

In some applications, an a-c signal is applied to the control electrode of the CRT. This causes the intensity of the beam to vary in step with the signal alternations. As a result, the trace is brightened during positive half-cycles and darkened or blanked-out during negative half-cycles.

This process, called *intensity modulation* or *Z-axis modulation* (in contrast to horizontal *X-axis* and vertical *Y-axis*), produces bright segments or dots on the trace in response to positive peaks, or dim segments or holes in response to negative peaks.

Intensity modulation is invaluable in many test procedures in which signals are applied simultaneously to the control electrode and one or both deflecting plates.

1.11 OSCILLOSCOPE BASIC LAYOUT

The simplest oscilloscope consists of CRT, power supply, focus control, and intensity control. Such an arrangement is sometimes used in applications, such as transmitter modulation checking from trapezoidal patterns, where high signal voltages are available for the deflecting plates and special sweep is not needed. Most oscilloscopes, however, are more complex than this, since their applications call for such complements as amplifiers, sweep generators, synchronizing circuits, and a calibration-voltage source.

To describe all combinations which are possible, and which in fact are found, in commercial oscilloscopes is beyond the scope of this book. Figure 1-9 shows the layout of the conventional *complete* instrument. This block diagram gives essential sections and channels; special-purpose oscilloscopes contain additional sections.

The CRT heater and the heaters of tubes in the amplifiers and sweep generator are powered by the a-c filament supply (A). This usually is nothing more than the filament windings on the main power transformer of the instrument. This section also supplies an accurate a-c calibrating voltage to terminal 1. CRT d-c voltage is obtained from the high-voltage d-c supply (B) through a voltage divider string, R_1 to R_5, inclusive. Note that R_3 in this string is a potentiometer for varying the focusing-electrode voltage and is the *focus control*, and that R_5 is a potentiometer for varying the control-

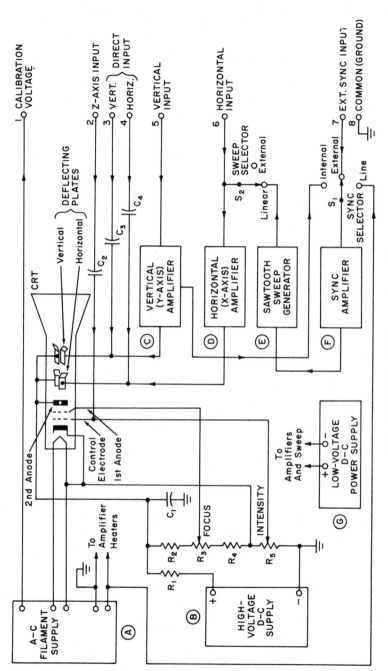

FIG. 1-9. The basic layout of an oscilloscope.

electrode voltage and is the *intensity control*. Capacitor C_1 grounds the deflecting plates and the 2nd anode for the signal voltage but d-c isolates these electrodes from ground. A somewhat different arrangement is used in a d-c oscilloscope. (Some instruments do not operate the deflecting plates against ground in this manner, but use push-pull amplifiers to excite both plates of each pair.) The low-voltage supply (G) provides d-c voltages for the amplifiers and sweep generators. Often, this latter supply is integral with high-voltage supply B.

Block C represents the vertical amplifier accessible through front-panel input terminal 5; D, the horizontal amplifier accessible through front-panel input terminal 6; E, the linear sawtooth sweep generator; and F, the sync amplifier accessible through front-panel input terminal 7. Although a single ground (common) input terminal is shown as 8 for simplicity, separate ground terminals are usually provided for the horizontal and vertical inputs. In addition to the amplifier input terminals, separate input terminals (3 and 4) provide direct input to the vertical and horizontal deflecting plates, respectively. Also, terminal 2 provides direct access to the control electrode for intensity (Z-axis) modulation. (In some oscilloscopes, there is also a Z-axis amplifier.) Capacitors C_2, C_3, and C_4 provide d-c blocking.

Normally, switch S_2 is set to its LINEAR position. This connects the sweep generator output to the horizontal amplifier input. The sweep voltage accordingly is amplified before being applied to the horizontal deflecting plates. When an externally generated sweep is desired, S_2 is thrown to its EXTERNAL position, and the external sweep generator is connected to input terminal 6. The sweep synchronizing voltage is applied to the internal sweep generator (E) through switch S_1, which permits selection of the type of sync. When S_1 is set to its EXTERNAL position, sync is obtained, through sync amplifier F, from an external sync signal source connected to input terminal 7. When S_1 is at INTERNAL, the test signal itself, entering the oscilloscope at vertical input terminal 5, is used to synchronize the sweep. When S_1 is at LINE, a low voltage of power-line frequency is taken from the a-c supply (usually from one of the filament windings of the transformer) to synchronize the sweep.

This simplified layout does not show gain controls of the various amplifiers, sweep frequency controls, sync polarity selector, beam centering controls, or astigmatism control. Presentation of the basic layout of the complete oscilloscope does not require their inclusion. The function and adjustment of all controls are given in the next chapter.

Signals may be applied to the vertical (Y) axis through the vertical amplifier via input terminal 5, or directly to the vertical deflecting plates via input terminal 3. Signals may be applied to the horizontal (X) axis through the horizontal amplifier via input terminal 6, with S_2 set to EXTERNAL to disable the internal sweep generator, or directly to the horizontal deflecting plates via input terminal 4. Signals may be applied to the Z-axis for intensity modulation via input terminal 2. A synchronizing signal may be applied to the internal sweep generator via input terminal 7 and the internal sync amplifier.

The calibrating voltage may be applied to the vertical axis by running a lead between terminals 1 and 5, or to the horizontal axis by running a lead between terminals 1 and 6.

Chapter 2

Oscilloscope Controls and Adjustments

This chapter deals with oscilloscope controls and their function in adjusting the instrument for a satisfactory display. In general, oscilloscope controls may be categorized as *functional controls* (those which are continually used, and usually found on the front panel) and *operating controls* (those used in the calibration and maintenance of the instrument, which usually must not be disturbed by the operator, and generally are found inside the case). We are concerned mainly with functional controls but will describe the purpose and nature of operating controls, as the operator should be aware of their role.

Not all controls will be found in any one type of instrument. For example, a simple, inexpensive oscilloscope will not have an ac-dc switch if its amplifiers handle ac only. Also, controls and terminals are not always found in the same place (one instrument has the Z-axis input terminal in the rear, whereas another has it on the front panel; direct input to deflecting plates is handled by a selector switch connected to the regular input terminal in one instrument, whereas it is handled by separate rear terminals in another). Expensive, special-purpose oscilloscopes often have more controls because these instruments provide more functions.

The controls and adjustments are discussed in the order in which they ordinarily come to the attention of the operator when an oscilloscope is set up and used. Sections 2.1 to 2.18, inclusive, discuss functional controls; Section 2.19 discusses important operating controls.

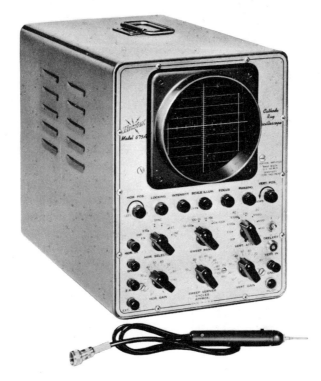

FIG. 2-1. A general-purpose, wideband oscilloscope. A low-capacitance probe rests
in front of the instrument. (See Fig.
2-2 for identification of the functional
controls on the front panel.) **Courtesy
of the Hickok Electrical Instrument Co.**

Figure 2-1 shows a general-purpose oscilloscope suitable for use
by the low-budget laboratory, electronic service technician, student,
lecturer, and radio amateur.[1] The bandwidth of its vertical channel
is dc to 4.5 megacycles.

Figure 2-2 identifies the front-panel controls and terminals seen
in the photograph, and keys these to applicable sections in this
chapter.

---

[1] Model 675A, The Hickok Electrical Instrument Co., Cleveland 8, Ohio.

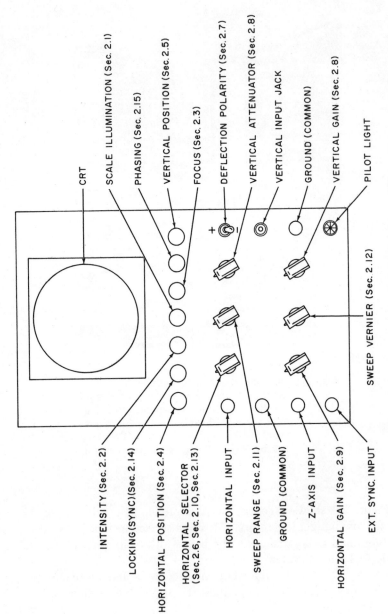

CRT

SCALE ILLUMINATION (Sec. 2.1)

PHASING (Sec. 2.15)

VERTICAL POSITION (Sec. 2.5)

FOCUS (Sec. 2.3)

DEFLECTION POLARITY (Sec. 2.7)

VERTICAL ATTENUATOR (Sec. 2.8)

VERTICAL INPUT JACK

GROUND (COMMON)

VERTICAL GAIN (Sec. 2.8)

PILOT LIGHT

INTENSITY (Sec. 2.2)

LOCKING (SYNC)(Sec. 2.14)

HORIZONTAL POSITION (Sec. 2.4)

HORIZONTAL SELECTOR
(Sec. 2.6, Sec. 2.10, Sec. 2.13)

HORIZONTAL INPUT

SWEEP RANGE (Sec. 2.11)

GROUND (COMMON)

Z-AXIS INPUT

HORIZONTAL GAIN (Sec. 2.9)

EXT. SYNC. INPUT

SWEEP VERNIER (Sec. 2.12)

FIG. 2-2. The functional controls of an oscilloscope.

2.1 SCREEN ILLUMINATION

In some oscilloscopes, the engraved lines of the transparent viewing screen are brightened by edge-lighting the graticule. This provides a sharp reproduction of the lines when photographs are made from the screen. A front-panel control is provided for adjusting the brightness of the illumination to suit individual conditions of viewing or photographing, or for extinguishing the light. The illumination does not ordinarily produce an interfering glare.

2.2 INTENSITY CONTROL

The intensity control potentiometer permits adjustment of trace brightness. A wide range is provided, extending from total darkness to very bright. Maximum intensity produces a spot or trace that is bright enough to burn the CRT screen permanently if it is allowed to remain in one position too long.

2.3 FOCUS CONTROL

The focus control potentiometer adjusts trace sharpness. Its wide range permits sharpening of the spot to a fine dot or broadening it to a fuzzy disc.

2.4 HORIZONTAL CENTERING CONTROL

The horizontal centering control potentiometer is also called *horizontal position control* or *X-position control*. Adjusting it moves the spot from side to side to any desired horizontal position on the screen.

2.5 VERTICAL CENTERING CONTROL

The vertical centering control potentiometer is also called *vertical position control* or *Y-position control*. Adjusting it moves the spot up and down to any desired vertical position on the screen.

2.6 AMPLIFIER SELECTOR

The amplifier selector is a switch for changing from a-c amplifier to d-c amplifier, or vice versa, in the horizontal or vertical deflection channel. Generally, the amplifier is direct-coupled. Basically, therefore, it is a d-c amplifier which will also handle ac; the switch inserts (for ac) or short-circuits (for dc) an input coupling capacitor. In an occasional instrument, the amplifier is capacitor-coupled, and therefore, basically, an a-c circuit; the switch cuts a chopper in or out for converting a d-c input signal to ac for presentation to the amplifier.

2.7 TRACE REVERSER

The trace reverser is a polarity-reversing switch which inverts the vertical deflection. In observation of certain signals (such as TV waveforms), the signal is often displayed upside down; it can be righted by throwing this switch.

The switch positions usually are labeled ($+$) for an upright pattern, and ($-$) for an inverted one.

2.8 VERTICAL GAIN CONTROL

The vertical gain control potentiometer is also called *V-gain (amplitude) control* or *Y-gain (amplitude) control*. Adjusting it, while holding the vertical input signal voltage constant, varies the height of the pattern on the screen.

Some vertical gain controls are more complicated than the single potentiometer. These are *attenuators* which consist of a step-type section and a potentiometer vernier section. The potentiometer provides continuously variable control of gain in any one of the ranges provided by the step-type ("coarse adjustment") section. The steps are integral, usually providing multipliers of $\times 0.1$, $\times 1$, $\times 10$, $\times 100$, and $\times 1000$ for the potentiometer setting. Such attenuators are frequency compensated for wideband response.

2.9 HORIZONTAL GAIN CONTROL

The horizontal gain control potentiometer is also called *H-gain (amplitude) control* or *X-gain (amplitude) control*. Adjusting it, while holding the horizontal input signal voltage constant, varies the width of the pattern on the screen.

Some horizontal gain controls are more complicated than the single potentiometer. These are *attenuators* which consist of a step-type ("coarse adjustment") section and a potentiometer (vernier or "fine adjustment") section. The potentiometer provides continuously variable control of gain in any of the ranges provided by the step-type section. As in the vertical attenuator, the steps are integral, usually providing multipliers of $\times 1$ and $\times 10$ for the potentiometer setting.

2.10 SWEEP SELECTOR

With the sweep selector switch, the operator may select the type of sweep to be used. In simple general-purpose oscilloscopes, the selection includes (1) linear sawtooth (internal), (2) external, and (3) line-frequency sine-wave (internal). (See S_2 in Fig. 1-9.) Some oscilloscopes do not have this switch.

In addition to the selections mentioned in the preceding paragraph, driven sweep, single sweep, delayed sweep, and similar variations are provided by some professional, laboratory-type oscilloscopes.

An oscilloscope designed for television servicing may provide, in addition to the usual sweep-frequency ranges, two preset fixed frequencies for TV alignment. One of these is 30 cps (TV vertical deflection frequency); the other is 7875 cps (TV horizontal deflection frequency).

In some oscilloscopes, the sweep selector and sync selector functions are combined in a single rotary switch.

2.11 SWEEP RANGE SELECTOR

The sweep range selector switch (often called *coarse frequency control)* permits selection of the frequency range of the internal sawtooth generator. Typical ranges provided in general-purpose oscilloscopes are 10-100 cps, 100-1000 cps, 1-10 kc, and 10-100 kc. A few such instruments provide sweep ranges up to 500 kc.

In professional, laboratory-type oscilloscopes, the sweep ranges often are expressed in time units (microseconds, milliseconds, or seconds per centimeter of screen width) instead of frequency. This is a labor saver, since the time interval of the display, rather than the sweep frequency, is of first importance in many scientific measurements, and time would have to be calculated from sweep frequency if it were not given directly. Typical ranges extend from 0.1 microseconds per centimeter to 5 sec/cm. In some instruments, sweep time is stated per scale division, rather than per centimeter.

2.12 SWEEP FREQUENCY CONTROL

The sweep frequency control potentiometer (often called *fine frequency control* or *frequency vernier*) permits continuous variation of sweep frequency within any of the ranges provided by the sweep range selector described in Section 2.11. With it, the frequency may be set closely to a desired value. In a simple oscilloscope, the scale of this control is graduated in arbitrary units (0-10 or 0-100); in a professional laboratory instrument, it may be direct reading in frequency or time units.

2.13 SYNC SELECTOR

With the sync selector, the operator may select the type of signal used to synchronize the sweep oscillator. The selections generally are (1) + internal; (2) − internal; (3) line-frequency sine-wave; and (4) external. (1) uses the positive half-cycle of the vertical input signal, (2) uses the negative half-cycle of this signal. (3) uses a low a-c voltage taken from the oscilloscope power supply. (4) uses a signal from an external generator via the self-contained sync amplifier.

In some oscilloscopes, the sync selector and sweep selector functions are combined in a single rotary switch.

2.14 SYNC AMPLITUDE CONTROL

The sync amplitude control potentiometer is the gain control of the self-contained sync amplifier, and its adjustment varies the amplitude of the synchronizing voltage applied to the internal sweep generator. At the correct setting of this control, the sawtooth sweep locks in step with the sync voltage, and the display stands still on the screen.

2.15 PHASING CONTROL

The phasing control potentiometer is the variable resistance arm of an RC phase-shifting network. Its adjustment varies the phase of the line-frequency sweep. This is an especially important adjustment when observing the response pattern of a tuned circuit or amplifier using a sweep signal generator that has a line-frequency sweep rate. When the oscilloscope is properly phased with the signal generator, the display becomes a single, stationary response curve. (Without correct phasing, double patterns will appear.)

2.16 Z-AXIS GAIN CONTROL

The Z-axis gain control potentiometer is the gain control of the Z-axis amplifier. (Also called *intensity modulation gain (amplitude) control*.) Its adjustment provides continuous variation of the intensity-modulation voltage. The voltage range provided by this control is sufficient to give intensity modulation varying all the way from zero to intense brightening on positive half-cycles or "hole punching" (complete blanking) on negative half-cycles.

2.17 CALIBRATION VOLTAGE CONTROL

Adjustment of the calibration voltage control potentiometer provides continuous variation of the amplitude of the internally generated calibration voltage. In the simplest case, the calibrating voltage is a line-frequency sine wave obtained from a filament winding of the oscilloscope power transformer and set to 1 volt peak-to-peak by means of a voltage divider. The calibration voltage control then allows this voltage to be adjusted between zero and 1 volt p-p. In other instruments, a line-frequency square wave is used. Some advanced oscilloscopes provide a square wave at a higher frequency, such as 1000 cps.

In some professional, laboratory-type oscilloscopes, the calibration voltage control is more complicated than the simple potentiometer. It consists of a step-type section (range selector) and potentiometer (fine, or vernier, control). The potentiometer may provide a smooth variation between zero and 10 v, while the step-type selector provides multipliers of $\times 0.001$, $\times 0.01$, $\times 0.1$, $\times 1$, and $\times 10$.

2.18 SWEEP MAGNIFICATION SELECTOR

Sweep magnification causes the displayed pattern to be widened (horizontally magnified) on the screen for closer observation of a part of the signal. It does this by multiplying the sweep period.

The sweep magnification selector usually is a selector switch, the scale of which reads direct in magnifications, such as $\times 1$, $\times 2$, $\times 5$, $\times 10$, $\times 20$, $\times 50$, and $\times 100$.

2.19 OPERATING CONTROLS

In addition to the functional controls discussed in Sections 2.1 to 2.18, there are other controls which must be adjusted for optimum performance of the oscilloscope. These controls are set during calibration of the instrument and require no further adjustment until the oscilloscope is being repaired or recalibrated. Hence, they are placed inside the instrument for protection against accident or tampering. The principal operating controls are listed below. They will not all be found in any one oscilloscope model. A special-purpose instrument, especially the professional, laboratory-type oscilloscope, will have additional controls for its special circuits.

Principal operating controls include the following: *Astigmatism* (spot size and shape); *Calibration Voltage* (setting of calibration voltage input to the calibration voltage control described in Section 2.17); *D-C Balance* (balancing of d-c amplifiers for initial spot centering); *Frequency Compensation* (adjustment of amplifier and attenuator components in horizontal and vertical channels for wideband response); *Hum Balance* (cancellation of interfering power supply hum); *Linearity* (adjustment for linear horizontal and vertical deflection on each side of center screen); *Sweep Frequency* (standardization of sawtooth generator, and presetting of TV spot frequencies in television oscilloscopes); and *Voltage Regulation* (setting of output voltage of regulated power supplies in oscilloscope).

Chapter 3

Oscilloscope Accessories

For most applications, the oscilloscope is used without external devices. In other uses, some attachment, such as a probe, is needed to modify the response of the instrument in some desired way or to modify the input signal. The operator must be familiar with these accessories if he is to use them profitably.

This chapter describes the principal accessories for oscilloscopes without going into unnecessary detail. These are the common attachments which increase the usefulness and dependability of the instrument. Additional accessories will be found wherever highly specialized tests and measurements must be made.

3.1 WHY SPECIAL PROBES ARE NEEDED

From experience with test meters, the technician knows that a probe functions simply as an extension of the meter terminal. Basically it is nothing more than a slender metallic prod on the end of an insulated rod (handle) connected to the instrument terminal through a flexible insulated lead. Through its use, the instrument can be connected to any circuit point which the prod touches. This is a probe in its simplest form.

The simple probe may be used to connect an oscilloscope quickly to any desired point in a test circuit. This is entirely satisfactory at dc and low audio frequencies and when the maximum amplification of the oscilloscope channels is not used. At high frequencies and/or high gain, however, the simple probe is inadequate: hand capacitance can cause hum pickup or attenuation of the signal amplitude, and the input impedance of the oscilloscope (which the probe transfers directly to the test point) may be low enough to load the test circuit. To minimize hand capacitance and stray coupling, the probe handle and lead must be carefully shielded; the capacitance between shielding and conductor must be minimal. To reduce loading effect by increasing the impedance of the instrument circuit a suitable series capacitor is built into the shielded probe (sometimes a series resistor is used).

Other special probes convert the signal to a form that may be handled and displayed by the oscilloscope. Thus, a *voltage-divider probe* reduces signal voltage to a safe level; a *demodulator probe* selects the modulating voltage from an a-m wave; and an *r-f probe* rectifies the radio-frequency voltage and delivers a d-c output proportional to the peak r-f voltage. Special probes are described in Sections 3.2, 3.3, 3.4, 3.5, and 3.6.

3.2 LOW-CAPACITANCE PROBE

The low-capacitance probe decreases the input capacitance of the measuring circuit. Its use insures that the circuit under test will be least disturbed by connection of the instrument. For example, without this probe, connection of the oscilloscope can completely detune a radio-frequency circuit.

Figure 3-1 shows the details of a low-capacitance probe. Resistors R_1 and R_2 and trimmer capacitor C are contained in the shielded handle and are preset by screwdriver adjustment. The resistances

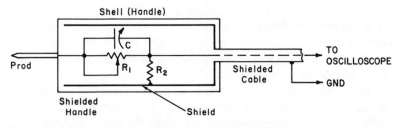

FIG. 3-1. A low-capacitance probe.

generally are selected such that, with the capacitance, they form a 10:1 voltage divider when the probe is connected to the oscilloscope vertical amplifier input. Capacitor C provides frequency compensation to preserve the frequency response of the oscilloscope. C and R_1 are factory-adjusted and need not be disturbed unless the probe is being recalibrated.

The values of C, R_1, and R_2 are chosen, with respect to the input impedance of the oscilloscope and the shunt capacitance of the shielded cable, so that the 10:1 voltage division and a 4:1 to 10:1 capacitance reduction are obtained. The operator using a voltage-calibrated oscilloscope must remember that voltage indications will be one-tenth of true values when the probe is attached.

Some low-capacitance probes are provided with a switch which at one setting short-circuits C and R_1 to give direct input to the oscilloscope (see the probe in Fig. 2-1). This permits the single probe to be used both for low-capacitance and straight-through input.

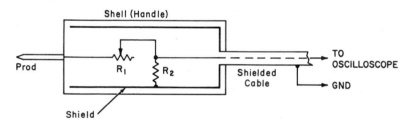

FIG. 3-2. A resistor-type, voltage-divider probe.

3.3 RESISTOR-TYPE VOLTAGE-DIVIDER PROBE

The maximum signal voltage which can be handled safely by the input channels of an oscilloscope depends upon the ratings of components and insulation in these channels. When higher voltages are to be checked, they must be reduced to a safe value by means of a voltage-divider probe (also called *high-voltage probe*).

One such probe employs a simple resistance voltage divider, as shown in Fig. 3-2. Resistors R_1 and R_2 are chosen in value, with respect to the input impedance of the oscilloscope vertical amplifier, so that the desired voltage step-down will be obtained (this usually is 10:1 or 100:1). The variable resistance R_1 may be set initially for exact division.

The low-capacitance probe (Fig. 3-1) may also be used, provided that its voltage division ratio is adequate. In addition to signal reduction, the low-capacitance probe provides flat frequency response because of its frequency compensation.

3.4 CAPACITOR-TYPE VOLTAGE-DIVIDER PROBE

The resistor-type probe described in the preceding section is unsuitable in some applications where the probe resistors set up a stray conduction path in the circuit under test. In such applications, a probe may be employed which contains a capacitive voltage divider.

In the probe shown in Fig. 3-3, voltage division is effected by capacitors C_1 and C_2. These capacitances are chosen, with respect to the shunting capacitance of the cable and the oscillosope input capacitance, to give the required voltage division. C_2 is made variable for initial adjustment of the output voltage to the exact desired value.

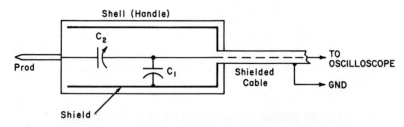

FIG. 3-3. A capacitor-type, voltage-divider probe.

3.5 DEMODULATOR PROBE

In order to display the low-frequency component (modulation envelope) of an amplitude-modulated signal, the signal must be demodulated before it is presented to the oscilloscope. This is accomplished with a demodulator probe (Fig. 3-4), which essentially is a diode detector.

In this probe, C is a low-capacitance dc-blocking capacitor which protects the germanium diode (D) from damage by any d-c component in the circuit under test. A shunt rectifier circuit is formed by C, D, and R_1. As a result of the action of this circuit, the diode detects (demodulates) the applied AM signal and developes a voltage across load resistor R_1 that has the waveform and frequency of the modulating voltage and is proportional to its amplitude. This action is the same as that of a diode radio detector which demodulates the radio signal and delivers the audio component. R_2 is an isolating resistor which minimizes loading effect of the probe and oscilloscope on the circuit under test.

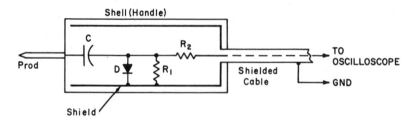

FIG. 3-4. A demodulator probe.

3.6 R-F PROBE

When the oscilloscope response is short of the r-f spectrum, radio-frequency voltages may be measured only if an r-f probe is attached. This probe rectifies the r-f energy and delivers a d-c output voltage which is almost equal to the peak r-f voltage. This d-c voltage is then applied to the oscilloscope d-c vertical input and measured on the calibrated viewing screen.

Figure 3-5 shows the structure of a typical r-f probe, which is similar in circuit to the modulator probe (Fig. 3-4). Here, however, blocking capacitor C has a much higher capacitance than the one used in the demodulator probe. It is rated between 0.02 and 0.05

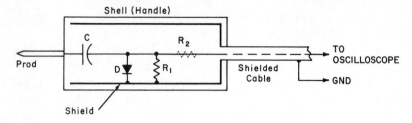

FIG. 3-5. An r-f probe.

μfd to insure peak-voltage operation of the shunt-diode rectifier circuit. Germanium diode D rectifies the r-f voltage and develops a d-c output voltage across load resistor R_1 equal to the peak r-f voltage minus the small forward drop across the diode. The resulting oscilloscope deflection is read as peak r-f voltage. When rms indications are desired, a series resistor (R_2) is included in the probe to drop the output voltage by the proper amount. This resistance is chosen with respect to the oscilloscope input resistance, so that a voltage division of 0.707 is provided.

3.7 D-C VOLTAGE CALIBRATOR

When the oscilloscope is used for voltage measurements, provision must be made for voltage-calibrating the screen. Some oscilloscopes supply an internally generated voltage for this purpose. A service-type instrument, for example, may supply a 1 volt peak-to-peak, line-frequency, sine-wave potential at a front-panel terminal (see Fig. 1-9). For calibration purposes, this voltage is applied to the input channel (usually, the vertical) and the gain control is adjusted to align the top and bottom of the pattern with calibration points on the graticule. A professional, laboratory-type oscilloscope might supply an internally generated 400- or 1000-cps square-wave voltage through an attenuator (coarse and fine) which reads directly in volts and millivolts. This adjustable calibrating voltage is applied to the vertical channel whenever the selector switch of the channel is set to its CALIBRATE position.

When an oscilloscope supplies no internal calibrating voltage, or one of unsuitable amplitude, an external source must be used. Both a-c and d-c continuously variable voltage calibrators are available for this purpose.

Figure 3-6 shows the details of a d-c voltage calibrator. This unit contains a closely regulated 100-v d-c supply and an attenuator consisting of potentiometer R_1 and a range selector (switch S and resistors R_2 to R_5). R_1 is direct-reading in voltage (0-100), and its indications are multiplied by 0.001, 0.01, 0.1, or 1, depending upon the setting of the switch. The output voltage indicated by the combined readings of the potentiometer and switch is the voltage presented to the oscilloscope. When S is set to its SIGNAL position, the signal under observation (applied to the SIGNAL INPUT terminals) is transmitted through the calibrator, minus the calibrating voltage, to the oscilloscope. This arrangement enables the operator to place on the screen, at will, the signal or calibrating voltage for calibration.

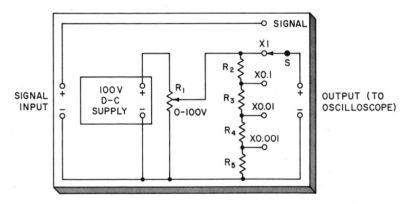

FIG. 3-6. A d-c voltage calibrator.

3.8 A-C VOLTAGE CALIBRATOR

An a-c voltage calibrator is similar to the d-c calibrator just described, except that the internal source supplies a voltage-regulated, line-frequency, square-wave signal at 100 v peak-to-peak.

The fine-control potentiometer (R_1 in Fig. 3-7) is direct-reading 0-100 v p-p, and this voltage is multiplied by the setting of switch S (0.001, 0.01, 0.1, or 1). The indicated value of peak-to-peak voltage is applied to the oscilloscope.

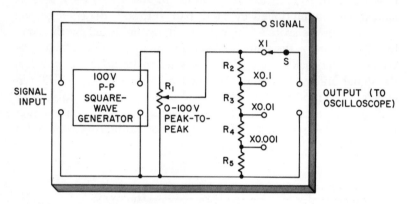

FIG. 3-7. An a-c voltage calibrator.

As with the d-c calibrator, when switch S is set to SIGNAL, the signal under study (applied to the SIGNAL INPUT terminals) is transmitted through the calibrator, minus the calibrating voltage, to the oscilloscope. This arrangement enables the operator to place on the screen, at will, the signal or the calibrating voltage for comparison.

3.9 FREQUENCY (TIME) CALIBRATOR

Some oscilloscopes supply an internally generated standard frequency for calibrating the sweep or time axis. This is a sine-wave or square-wave voltage of accurate frequency. The calibrating voltage may be applied to the vertical input, and the sweep frequency and sync adjusted for a single stationary cycle on the screen.

Common frequencies are 1000 cps (1 cycle = 1 millisecond), 100 kc (1 cycle = 10 microseconds), and 1 mc (1 cycle = 1 microsecond).

3.10 ELECTRONIC SWITCH

The *electronic switch* is a device which enables two signals to be displayed simultaneously on the screen of a single-gun CRT. (Electronic switches have also been designed for more than two displays.) This performance is a convenience, since it permits the direct comparison of two signals without necessitating a multiple-gun tube.

Some advanced professional oscilloscopes have self-contained electronic switches. But less costly instruments do not offer this feature, and an external electronic switch must be used with them.

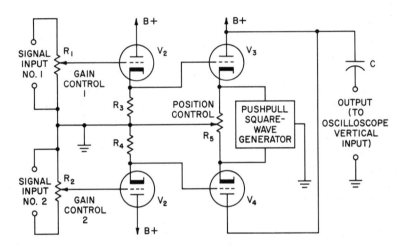

FIG. 3-8. An electronic switch.

Figure 3-8 shows the skeleton circuit of an electronic switch. Here, V_1 and V_2 are amplifier tubes, and V_3 and V_4 are switching tubes. Input signal No. 1 is applied to amplifier V_1 through gain control R_1; input signal No. 2 is applied to V_2 through R_2. The square-wave generator alternately biases first V_1 and then V_2 to cutoff. When V_1 is cut off, V_2 is conducting and transmits input signal No. 2 to the OUTPUT terminals. Conversely, when V_2 is cut off, V_1 is conducting and transmits input signal No. 1 to the OUTPUT terminals. When the square-wave switching frequency is much higher than either signal frequency, bits of each signal are alternately presented to

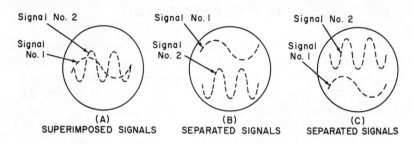

FIG. 3-9. Oscilloscope display through an
electronic switch.

the oscilloscope vertical input to reproduce the two signals on the screen.

Figure 3-9 shows some typical two-signal displays afforded by the electronic switch. The traces are composed of tiny segments representing the switching intervals, but when the switching rate is fast enough, the segments are so small that a solid line is seen. In Fig. 3-9A, the traces are laid on top of each other for easy comparison by adjustment of the POSITION CONTROL potentiometer (R_5 in Fig. 3-8). In Fig. 3-9B and C, the traces have been separated by readjustment of R_5. The traces may be shifted vertically with respect to each other to any desired position for easy comparison of amplitude, phase, and frequency, and their individual heights may be adjusted by means of gain controls R_1 and R_2.

3.11 EXTERNAL AMPLIFIERS

Although high-gain amplifiers are employed in an oscilloscope, some signals are too weak to produce a large enough pattern. In order to accommodate these signals, external amplification must be provided.

An auxiliary amplifier must supply the required extra gain and must have frequency response identical with that of the oscilloscope channel into which it feeds. The shortest possible leads should be used to connect it to the oscilloscope, and these should be shielded if practicable.

Conventional external amplifiers of the wideband type supply voltage gains of 20 db and 40 db that can be selected with a switch.

Chapter 4

General Oscilloscope Operating Procedure

Succeeding chapters give specific instructions for use of the oscilloscope in various types of tests and measurements. This chapter, however, is devoted entirely to an outline of good operating practice. The reader is urged to adopt the rules and procedures given here.

The benefits of good practice are manifold. Foremost among them are increased accuracy of measurement, reduced labor and time, protection of instrument and operator, lengthened life of instrument, and enhanced enjoyment of test work.

Instructions and procedures given here will not be repeated in subsequent chapters. Instructions in those chapters will presuppose the reader's familiarity with this material and his expertness in applying it.

4.1 HOW TO PLACE AN OSCILLOSCOPE INTO OPERATION

Even a simple oscilloscope costs a respectable amount of money, a good reason to protect the instrument from damage and to insist upon top performance. Aside from economic considerations, it must be agreed that a damaged oscilloscope is an unreliable instrument. The operator, therefore, must take every precaution to protect the oscilloscope and the circuit to which it is connected. Properly placing the instrument into operation protects both.

Oscilloscope Setup Procedure

1. Set POWER switch to OFF.

2. Turn INTENSITY, FOCUS, GAIN, and SYNC controls to lowest settings.

3. Switch-off internal sweep.

4. Set SWEEP selector to EXTERNAL.

5. Set HORIZONTAL and VERTICAL POSITION controls to mid-range.

6. Plug into power line.

7. Set POWER switch to ON.

8. After a one-minute warmup wait, advance INTENSITY control until spot appears on screen. To prevent burning of screen, use lowest intensity needed to see spot. If spot is not seen, it probably is off screen — reset POSITION controls to bring it into view.

9. Adjust FOCUS control to sharpen spot to fine point.

10. Adjust POSITION controls to position spot at exact center of screen.

11. Set SWEEP SELECTOR to INTERNAL (LINEAR).

12. Switch-on internal sweep and adjust SWEEP FREQUENCY control for any frequency higher than 100 cps.

13. Advance HORIZONTAL GAIN control, noting that spot is deflected into a horizontal line. Note also that length of line is controllable by adjustment of HORIZONTAL GAIN control.

14. Switch-off sweep and reduce horizontal gain to zero.

15. Advance VERTICAL GAIN control to mid-range.

16. Touch VERTICAL INPUT terminal, noting that stray signal pickup by hand causes spot to be deflected to give a vertical line. Note also that length of line is controllable by adjusting VERTICAL GAIN control.

17. Reduce vertical gain to zero.

18. Switch-on internal sweep and advance HORIZONTAL GAIN control for a horizontal-line trace.

19. Connect any required probe to the VERTICAL INPUT terminals.

20. Oscilloscope now is placed properly into operation and is ready for connection to the test circuit.

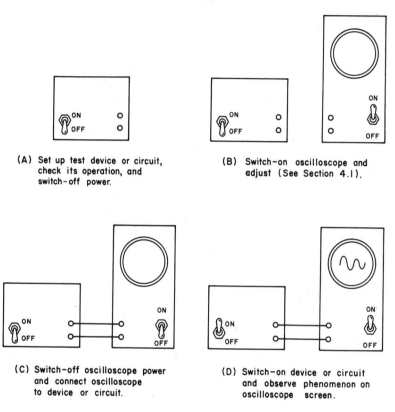

(A) Set up test device or circuit, check its operation, and switch-off power.

(B) Switch-on oscilloscope and adjust (See Section 4.1).

(C) Switch-off oscilloscope power and connect oscilloscope to device or circuit.

(D) Switch-on device or circuit and observe phenomenon on oscilloscope screen.

FIG. 4-1. Basic steps in the use of any oscilloscope.

If the oscilloscope is a d-c instrument with direct-coupled amplifiers, the waiting period in Step 8 will be longer than the prescribed one minute, because the amplifiers drift when started cold and take some time to stabilize. A five-minute period is safe in most cases. Some direct-coupled oscilloscopes continue to drift, at a progressively decreasing rate, up to one or two hours after they have been switched on. Consult the manufacturer's instruction manual for stabilization time.

A good operator will go through the 19 steps given above in sequence each time that he places his oscilloscope into operation unless he is the only person who uses the instrument. When other persons use the oscilloscope, he cannot be certain that position, intensity, and focus controls are at safe settings, and he will run the risk of damaging the instrument by switching it on immediately.

4.2 OPERATING PRECAUTIONS

Certain operating precautions apply to the operation of *any* oscilloscope:

1. Study the manufacturer's instruction manual thoroughly before attempting to use the oscilloscope. Do this even if you have had experience with other oscilloscopes.

2. Always place the instrument into operation according to the steps given in Section 4.1. Never connect the instrument to the test circuit until these steps are completed.

3. Switch the test-circuit power off until all connections to the oscilloscope are completed.

4. Use the minimum intensity necessary for comfortable viewing or efficient photographing. Do not operate the oscilloscope in bright sunlight.

5. Keep the spot moving on the screen. When it must stand still, reduce intensity to keep the screen from burning.

6. Unless the CRT is flat-faced, make all measurements in the center area, or reading errors will be caused by distortion in the curved periphery.

7. Always connect the GROUND (COMMON) terminal of the oscilloscope to the ground, or low-potential, point in the test circuit. Do this *before* connecting the high input terminal. Disconnect the instrument in the opposite sequence.

    CAUTION: *When both points in the test circuit are above ground, the metal case of the oscilloscope will be connected to high voltage and could deliver a dangerous electric shock.*

8. Use only shielded probes, and keep the fingers well away from the metal prod or tip.

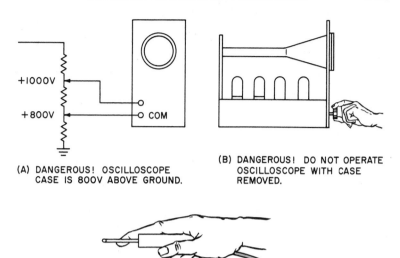

(A) DANGEROUS! OSCILLOSCOPE
    CASE IS 800V ABOVE GROUND.

(B) DANGEROUS! DO NOT OPERATE
    OSCILLOSCOPE WITH CASE
    REMOVED.

(C) DANGEROUS! DO NOT ALLOW FINGER TO
    TOUCH METAL PROD OF TEST PROBE.

FIG. 4-2. Precautions in oscilloscope operation.

9. Your oscilloscope is shielded; nevertheless, you should keep it clear of strong magnetic fields. Such fields can distort the display.

10. Never operate the instrument at a higher line voltage or different power frequency than that recommended by the manufacturer.

11. Keep all input-signal voltages below the specified maximum.

12. Never operate the instrument outside of its case without being extra careful. Many circuit points which thus would be exposed carry dangerously high voltage. Another hazard is the CRT, which can implode and scatter glass with great force.

13. Observe all of the well-known electrical safety rules when working with an oscilloscope.

14. Protect the instrument from vibration and mechanical shock.

15. Be sure that any internal fan or blower is operating.

16. Clean ventilating air filters regularly.

17. Replace the CRT when a bright trace no longer can be obtained or when spots have been burned into the face. Replace small

tubes and/or make repairs as soon as degraded or intermittent operation is noticed.

18. Leave repairs and adjustments to a skilled instrument technician. If you must adjust the operating controls, first study the oscilloscope manufacturer's instructions carefully.

19. The oscilloscope is not a plaything. Neither participate in nor condone pranks and horseplay with this instrument.

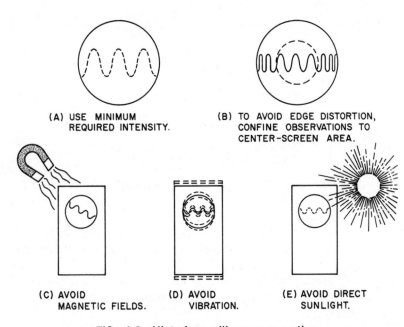

(A) USE MINIMUM REQUIRED INTENSITY.

(B) TO AVOID EDGE DISTORTION, CONFINE OBSERVATIONS TO CENTER-SCREEN AREA.

(C) AVOID MAGNETIC FIELDS.

(D) AVOID VIBRATION.

(E) AVOID DIRECT SUNLIGHT.

FIG. 4-3. Hints for oscilloscope operation.

4.3 INSTRUMENT, TEST-CIRCUIT RELATIONSHIP

For maximum benefit from use of the oscilloscope, the operator must be thoroughly familiar with the circuit under test and must have some idea of the voltage, frequency, and waveform to be expected at each test point. This will enable setting of the instrument controls for best display, with a minimum of blind searching.

When several oscilloscopes are available, select the one which will permit the greatest range of measurements on the test circuit. Thus, for testing an industrial control circuit in which the actuating signals are a composite of dc, af, and modulated rf, a wide-band oscilloscope having direct-coupled amplifiers and a low-capacitance probe would be chosen.

A competent technician will not waste time with an unsuitable meter. Neither will he do so with an inadequate oscilloscope. There is very little point, for example, in attempting to check a 2 mc signal with an audio oscilloscope having 200 kc bandwidth. To be sure, some small deflection might be obtained, but it would serve no quantitative purpose. Neither will a sensible technician *continuously* waste a 50 mc oscilloscope in testing audio amplifiers.

Chapter 5

Voltage and Current Measurement

A conventional CRT with calibrated screen is fundamentally an electrostatic voltmeter. The oscilloscope, therefore, may be used directly as a v-t voltmeter and indirectly as a current meter. But, unlike other electronic meters, the oscilloscope can show waveform, frequency, and phase, as well as amplitude of a current or voltage. Still another advantage is the exceedingly fast response of the oscilloscope.

Use of the oscilloscope as a wideband, high-impedance a-c voltmeter may avoid the inherent error introduced when a meter which has been calibrated on a sine-wave basis is used to measure a signal having significant harmonic content. This is so because voltage is measured from the displayed wave with the oscilloscope.

In spite of its utility, however, the oscilloscope is not a precision voltmeter; in much work of a routine or practical nature, it certainly could not be used economically in place of a simpler and less expensive meter. Its importance rests in its wide frequency response, lack of inertia, ability to display waveform, and because it can indicate voltage in addition to, and simultaneously with, other phenomena.

5.1 HOW TO VOLTAGE-CALIBRATE THE SCREEN

Before an oscilloscope can be used for direct measurement of voltage or current, its screen must be calibrated. The calibration procedure depends upon the type of oscilloscope and whether or not an external calibrating source must be used. Recommended procedures

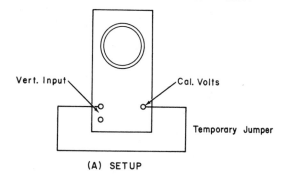

FIG. 5-1. Calibration with internal single
voltage.

are given below. In each example, the instruction "set up the oscilloscope" means to place the instrument into operation following the
procedures given in Section 4.1.

Calibration Procedure—With Internal Single-Voltage A-C Source

1. Set up oscilloscope.

2. Connect jumper between CALIBRATION VOLTAGE terminal and VERTICAL INPUT terminal (Fig. 5-1A).

3. Advance VERTICAL GAIN control for readable pattern.

4. Set SYNC selector to INTERNAL.

5. Adjust sweep frequency and SYNC control for several stationary cycles (Fig. 5-1B).

6. Adjust HORIZONTAL GAIN control to spread this pattern, as desired, on screen.

7. Adjust VERTICAL GAIN control to align tips of positive
half-cycles and tips of negative half-cycles with corresponding
marked calibration lines on screen.

The instrument is now calibrated. The calibration voltage usually is 1 v peak-to-peak, so the vertical distance between the points represents 1 v p-p. The VERTICAL ATTENUATOR, if present, will multiply indications in this range by 0.1, 1, 10, etc., depending upon the setting.

The manufacturer's instruction manual generally specifies the setting of the VERTICAL GAIN control (or VERTICAL ATTENUATOR) for calibration. The gain control always must be returned to the calibration setting when direct voltage measurements are to be made.

Some oscilloscopes do not bring the calibrating voltage to a panel terminal. Instead, this voltage is transmitted internally to the vertical channel when the VERTICAL SELECTOR switch is set to its CALIBRATE position. (See, for example, the VERTICAL ATTENUATOR in Fig. 2-1.)

The VERTICAL GAIN control may also be set to spread the calibration voltage over any desired vertical length. Thus, if this control is set for deflection of one division above and below the zero line for 1 v p-p, as shown in Fig. 5-1B, each scale division *at that setting of the gain control* represents 0.5 v p-p. If a subsequently applied test signal occupies 10 divisions, as shown in Fig. 5-1C, its voltage then is read as 5 v p-p. Some oscilloscopes, such as RCA Type WO-91A, have a graticule reading direct in volts, these indications being multiplied by settings of the vertical attenuator.

With the internal sweep switched-off, a single vertical line is obtained instead of the a-c cycles. The length of the line is proportional to the voltage.

Professional, laboratory-type oscilloscopes provide an internally generated, continuously variable, square-wave calibrating voltage. No external connections are required. The following procedure should be followed to calibrate the screen with this arrangement:

Calibration Procedure—With Internal Variable-Voltage A-C Source

1. Set up oscilloscope.

2. Set VERTICAL SELECTOR to CALIBRATE.

3. Switch-on calibrator.

4. Set internal sweep to lower frequency than that of calibrator.

5. Set VERTICAL GAIN control to desired operating position.

6. Adjust CALIBRATOR control to align flat peaks of square wave with the desired vertical scale divisions (see Fig. 5-2A).

7. Adjust SYNC control for stationary pattern, with SYNC SELECTOR set to INTERNAL.

8. Read peak-to-peak voltage from scale of CALIBRATOR control.

In Fig. 5-2, the calibrating voltage has been adjusted for deflection of two divisions above and below the zero line. If the voltage is read from the CALIBRATION control as 4 v p-p, the resulting screen calibration figure is 1 v p-p/div. (The full vertical axis shown in the illustration—20 divisions—thus would represent 20 v p-p.)

P-P CAL. VOLTAGE (Read from CAL. CONTROL)

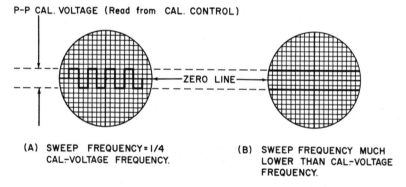

(A) SWEEP FREQUENCY=1/4 CAL.-VOLTAGE FREQUENCY.

(B) SWEEP FREQUENCY MUCH LOWER THAN CAL.-VOLTAGE FREQUENCY.

FIG. 5-2. Internal-calibrator patterns.

When the sweep frequency (f_s) is set to equal the frequency of the calibrating voltage (f_c), a single square-wave cycle will be seen; when f_s is lower than f_c, several cycles will appear (as in Fig. 5-2A); and when f_s is much lower than f_c, the vertical lines of the pattern will become obscured and the flat peaks will merge to form two horizontal lines (as in Fig. 5-2B). If the internal sweep is switched-off, a single vertical line is obtained, its length indicating the voltage.

When the square wave is applied to the d-c vertical amplifier, its peak above the zero line indicates positive voltage, and its peak below the zero line indicates negative voltage. Each of these voltages is equal to the *peak ac* (½ peak-to-peak) indicated by the CALIBRATOR control. Thus, Fig. 5-2 would show a deflection of +2 v and —2 v dc.

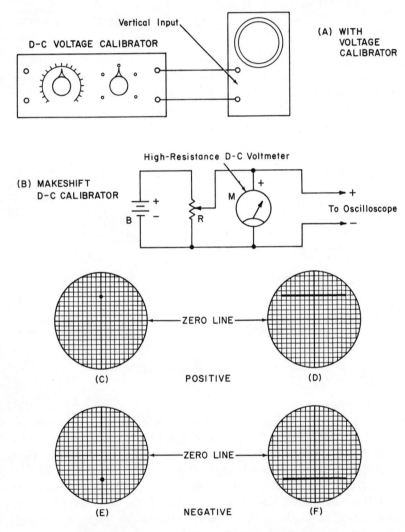

FIG. 5-3. D-C calibration with an external source.

When the oscilloscope provides no internal calibrating voltage, an external source must be used. Voltage calibrators suitable for this purpose are described in Sections 3.7 and 3.8.

Calibration Procedure—With External Source

For d-c voltage calibration:

1. Set up d-c oscilloscope.

2. Switch-off internal sweep.

3. Connect d-c calibrator, as shown in Fig. 5-3A.

4. Set calibrator controls for desired calibrating voltage.

5. Adjust VERTICAL GAIN control to move spot vertically up to the desired number of screen divisions. Thus, the five-division deflection in Fig. 5-3C indicates a positive voltage of the value shown by settings of the calibrator controls.

6. Reverse the leads to the oscilloscope, noting that the same deflection occurs vertically downward, as in Fig. 5-3E. This indicates a negative voltage of the value shown by settings of the calibrator controls.

7. When the internal sweep is switched-on, a horizontal line trace is obtained and this line moves above or below the zero line to indicate a positive voltage (Fig. 5-3D) or negative voltage (Fig. 5-3F), respectively.

If a calibrator is not available, a battery, potentiometer, and high-resistance voltmeter may be used (Fig. 5-3B), the calibrating voltage being adjusted with potentiometer R and read from meter M.

For a-c voltage calibration:

1. Set up oscilloscope.

2. Switch-on internal sweep.

3. Connect a-c calibrator, as shown in Fig. 5-4A.

4. Set calibrator controls for desired calibrating voltage.

5. Adjust VERTICAL GAIN control to spread square-wave pattern vertically between desired screen divisions. The pattern will resemble Fig. 5-2A or B, depending upon sweep frequency. This deflection corresponds to voltage indicated by settings of calibrator controls.

If a calibrator is not available, a transformer, potentiometer, and high-impedance voltmeter may be used (Fig. 5-4B), the calibrating voltage being adjusted with potentiometer R and read from meter M.

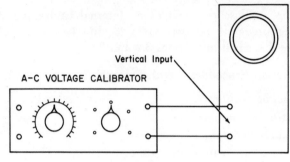

(A) WITH VOLTAGE CALIBRATOR

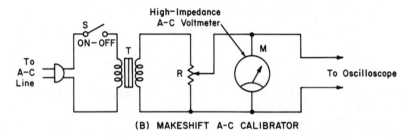

(B) MAKESHIFT A-C CALIBRATOR

FIG. 5-4. A-C calibration with an external source.

5.2 DIRECT MEASUREMENT OF VOLTAGE

In direct measurement of voltage, a calibrated oscilloscope is used like a voltmeter. The instrument must previously have been voltage-calibrated following one of the methods outlined in Section 5.1. Use short leads between oscilloscope and voltage source.

To measure a-c voltage:

1. Set up calibrated oscilloscope.
2. Switch-on internal sweep.
3. Set SYNC switch to INTERNAL.
4. Set VERTICAL GAIN control to position used in calibration.
5. Connect VERTICAL INPUT terminals to test-voltage source.
6. Adjust sweep frequency for several cycles on screen.

7. Adjust HORIZONTAL GAIN control to spread pattern over as much of screen as desired. Pattern will resemble Fig. 5-1C.

8. Count number of screen divisions between positive peak (tip) and negative peak.

9. Determine voltage by multiplying number of divisions by calibration figure (peak-to-peak volts/division). This gives peak-to-peak value of unknown voltage.

10. If voltage is sinusoidal, multiply this value by 0.5 for peak voltage, by 0.3535 for rms voltage, or by 0.318 for average voltage.

11. If a low-capacitance probe is attached to oscilloscope, multiply indicated voltage by probe ratio. For example, if probe reduction ratio is 10:1, multiply indicated voltage by 10.

To measure d-c voltage:

1. Set up calibrated d-c oscilloscope.

2. Switch-on internal sweep.

3. Set SYNC switch to INTERNAL.

4. Set VERTICAL GAIN control to position used during calibration.

5. Adjust HORIZONTAL GAIN control to lengthen horizontal-line trace on screen.

6. Connect VERTICAL INPUT terminals to test-voltage source.

7. Count number of divisions over which line was moved, up or down, from the zero line by test voltage.

8. Determine voltage by multiplying number of divisions by calibration figure (v/div.). Positive voltage deflects trace upward; negative voltage deflects it downward.

5.3 VOLTAGE MEASUREMENT WITH VOLTAGE CALIBRATOR

The advantage of this method is that it does not require a precalibrated screen, and the vertical gain control may be set anywhere in its range. The voltage calibrator may be either internal or external.

Follow this procedure:

1. Set up oscilloscope.

2. Set SYNC switch to INTERNAL.

3. Apply signal to oscilloscope vertical input.

4. Set internal sweep frequency for desired number of signal cycles in pattern.

5. Set SYNC control for stationary pattern.

6. Adjust VERTICAL GAIN control for desired height and HORIZONTAL GAIN control for desired width of pattern.

7. Carefully note peak-to-peak height of pattern.

8. Without disturbing vertical gain, switch-on calibrator. Signal disappears and is replaced by square-wave calibration pattern on screen.

9. Adjust CALIBRATOR control(s) until square wave fills same vertical space that signal filled.

10. Read peak-to-peak voltage from setting of calibrator control(s).

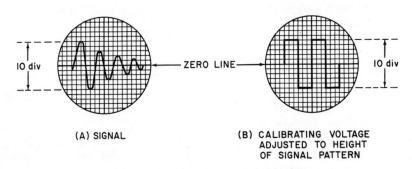

(A) SIGNAL

(B) CALIBRATING VOLTAGE ADJUSTED TO HEIGHT OF SIGNAL PATTERN

FIG. 5-5. A comparison of signal and calibrating voltages.

Figure 5-5 shows how the signal and calibrator voltages are compared on the screen in this manner. In Fig. 5-5A, the signal is a damped wave; its maximum peak-to-peak amplitude is to be measured. The maximum deflection is seen to occupy 10 divisions. After the calibrator is switched-in, the square-wave voltage is adjusted for the same deflection (see Fig. 5-5B). The unknown voltage is then read from the settings of the calibrator control(s).

When working with d-c signals, both the signal and calibrator voltages will be represented by a deflected dot (Fig. 5-3C or E) or deflected line (Fig. 5-3D or F).

With this method, a signal display may be interrupted as often as necessary and its voltage quickly checked, after which the signal display may be restored to the screen and the calibrator voltage removed. The technician does this frequently while making observations with the oscilloscope.

5.4 MEASURING PULSATING VOLTAGE

Pulsating dc contains only positive half-cycles or negative half-cycles. The output of a rectifier has such a waveform. So does the output of a d-c generator.

Figure 5-6A shows a positive pulsating voltage; Fig. 5-6B shows a negative pulsating voltage. Note in each instance that the peak amplitude is four and one-half divisions. This amplitude may be evaluated by determining what voltage corresponds to four and one-half divisions.

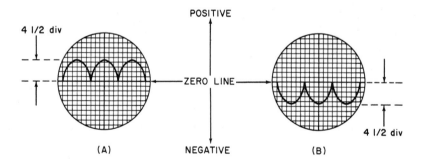

FIG. 5-6. Pulsating voltages.

Direct Method. Use a calibrated screen according to the method explained in Section 5.2. The value obtained will be *peak* voltage (since only one peak is present: positive in Fig. 5-6A, negative in Fig. 5-6B), although the screen calibration is given in peak-to-peak voltage.

Indirect Method. Use a voltage calibrator according to the method explained in Section 5.3. If calibrator is a-c type, the voltage value obtained will be peak-to-peak and must be divided by two to give the peak value of the pulsation. If calibrator is d-c type, the voltage value obtained (read from d-c scale of calibrator) equals peak value of the pulsation, and no calculation is required.

Increased stability of the zero line will be secured if a d-c oscilloscope is used for these measurements.

5.5 MEASURING FLUCTUATING (COMPOSITE) VOLTAGE

A fluctuating voltage, also called composite voltage, consists of an ac superimposed upon a dc. Plate voltage of a tube amplifying an a-c signal, or collector voltage of a transistor amplifying an a-c signal is fluctuating. This type of voltage is measured best with a d-c oscilloscope.

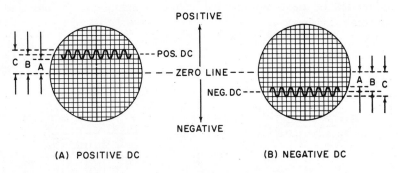

FIG. 5-7. Fluctuating voltages.

Figure 5-7 shows displays obtained with fluctuating voltages. In Fig. 5-7A, the positive d-c component of the fluctuating voltage produces a deflection to the fourth line above zero. The a-c component swings this voltage above the d-c line and below the d-c line (one division in each direction); i. e., from the 5th line (positive half-cycle) to the 3rd line (negative half-cycle). In Fig. 5-7B, the a-c and d-c voltage components are the same as in the preceding example, but the d-c component is negative and this deflects the entire pattern downward by the same amount as before.

Measure the various components of the fluctuating voltage by either (1) the direct method, using a dc-calibrated screen (Section 5.2) or (2) the indirect method, using a d-c voltage calibrator (Section 5.3) to check points *A*, *B*, and *C*. In Fig. 5-7A, the d-c voltage corresponds to four divisions, and the peak-to-peak a-c voltage to two divisions (i.e., from a deflection of five div. to the tip of the positive half-cycle to three div. to the tip of the negative half-cycle). If the direct screen calibration were 10 v/div., for example, the following values would be obtained: d-c component +40 v, a-c component 20 v p-p (7.07 v rms). Values are numerically the same in Fig. 5-7B, but the polarity is reversed; i. e., the d-c component is —40 v, and the a-c component oscillates about negative values.

5.6 MEASURING A-C AND D-C CURRENT

Current may be checked with a voltmeter by measuring the voltage drop (E) produced by the unknown current (I) flowing through an accurately known resistance (R), and calculating I = E/R. The oscilloscope is used in the same way: to measure the voltage drop across a shunt resistor.

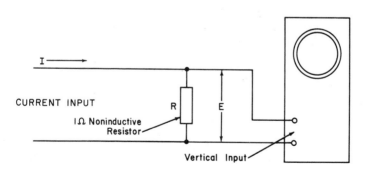

FIG. 5-8. The correct setup for current measurement.

Figure 5-8 shows the equipment setup for current measurement. To simplify calculations, a 1-ohm resistor is used. This must be a noninductive unit with a wattage rating numerically equal to twice the square of the maximum current (in amperes) to be measured.

To measure current:

1. Set up oscilloscope.

2. Connect 1-ohm shunt resistor (R), as shown in Fig. 5-8.

3. Pass unknown a-c or d-c current through R.

4. Measure voltage drop (E) across R, using either of the methods explained in Sections 5.2 or 5.3. For peak current determine peak voltage; for rms current, determine rms voltage; for average current, determine average voltage.

5. From this, calculate the current: $I = E$, where I is in amperes and E is in volts.

If the current is pulsating, use the voltage measurement method explained in Section 5.4.

5.7 MEASURING FLUCTUATING (COMPOSITE) CURRENT

If the current is fluctuating:

1. Use the voltage measurement method given in Section 5.5, checking first the d-c voltage drop (E_{dc}) and then the a-c voltage drop (E_{ac}).

2. Convert the a-c voltage to the rms value (E_{ac}).

3. Calculate the a-c and d-c currents separately:

$$I_{ac} = E_{ac}, \text{ and } I_{dc} = E_{dc}$$

4. Finally, calculate the total current:

$$I_t = \sqrt{E_{ac}^2 + E_{dc}^2}$$

5.8 OSCILLOSCOPE CURRENT PROBE

An amplifier-type *oscilloscope current probe* acts as a current pickup and operates into the vertical channel of the oscilloscope. It requires no direct connection to the circuit under test. A typical current probe operating into an instrument with 50 mv/div. calibration gives current response of 1 ma/div. to 1 amp/div. in 10 ranges. Current probe use is discussed in Volume 2.

Chapter 6

Frequency Measurement and Comparison

The oscilloscope is a sensitive indicator in frequency checking because of its utilization of the patterns known as *Lissajous figures.* (It is used for frequency measurement by other methods also.) The techniques are simple and the results are dependable. Measurements may be made at any frequency in the response range of the oscilloscope. High-amplitude signals outside of the amplifier passband may be applied directly to the deflecting plates.

This chapter describes principal methods of frequency measurement. The method selected for a particular purpose generally depends upon screen size, nature of standard frequency source, and whether or not the oscilloscope has Z-axis input.

6.1 USE OF LISSAJOUS FIGURES

The use of Lissajous figures permits the comparison of one frequency with another. The unknown frequency may be measured in terms of a known one, or one frequency may be adjusted to equal the other with no knowledge of the values of either one.

One frequency is applied to the oscilloscope horizontal channel, the other to the vertical channel, as shown in Fig. 6-1. Either signal may be applied to either channel; commonly, however, the unknown is presented to the vertical, and the known (standard) to the horizontal. For convenience in the following explanations, the horizontal signal is designated f_h, and the vertical signal is designated f_v.

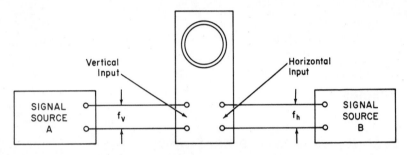

FIG. 6-1. The test setup for Lissajous figures.

Measurement Procedure

1. Set up oscilloscope.

2. Switch-off internal sweep.

3. Switch-off sync.

4. Connect signal sources to oscilloscope, as shown in Fig. 6-1.

5. Advance HORIZONTAL and VERTICAL GAIN controls, noting that pattern (very likely spinning) appears on screen.

6. Set HORIZONTAL and VERTICAL GAIN controls for desired width and height of pattern.

7. While holding frequency f_v constant, vary frequency f_h, noting that pattern spins in alternate directions and changes shape.

8. The pattern stands still whenever f_h and f_v are in integral ratio (either even or odd).

9. When $f_h = f_v$, pattern stands still and (if each signal is sinusoidal) is a single circle or ellipse (Fig. 6-2A).

10. When $f_v = 2f_h$, a two-loop horizontal pattern (Fig. 6-2B) appears.

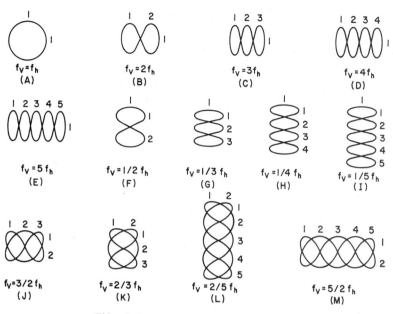

FIG. 6-2. Typical Lissajous figures.

To determine the frequency from any Lissajous figure, count the number of horizontal loops in the pattern and use this number for the numerator of a fraction; then count the number of vertical loops and use that number as the denominator; and finally multiply f_h (known frequency) by the fraction. Thus, in Fig. 6-2H, there is 1 horizontal loop and 4 vertical loops, giving a fraction of ¼. The unknown frequency (f_v), therefore, is ¼ f_h. Figure 6-2 shows some common Lissajous figures, with the loops numbered for illustrative purposes.

An accurately calibrated, variable-frequency oscillator will supply the horizontal search frequency for frequency measurement. When two frequencies are to be matched, and absolute frequency value is of no interest, either one may be applied to the vertical channel, and the variable-frequency one adjusted for the 1:1 pattern in Fig. 6-2A.

Use of Lissajous figures is limited by the number of loops which can be observed and counted on the screen. As the number increases, counting becomes progressively difficult. Accuracy is enhanced by a large screen, sharp focusing, steady display, and keen eyesight.

6.2 USE OF MODULATED-RING PATTERN

When a Lissajous figure contains a large number of loops, accurate counting becomes difficult. Figure 6-3 shows a test method that uses a modulated-ring pattern in place of the looped figure and permits a higher count. This pattern (Fig. 6-3B and C) is also called a *gear wheel* or *toothed wheel*, from its shape. The unknown frequency is determined by multiplying the known frequency by the number of teeth in the pattern. A large number of teeth may be formed on a circle spread over most of the screen.

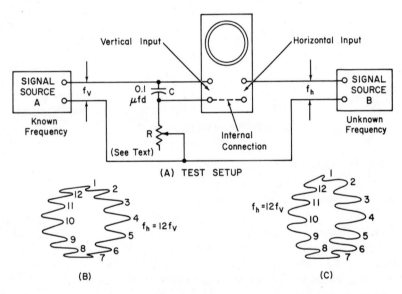

FIG. 6-3. The modulated-ring method.

Figure 6-3A shows the equipment setup. Here, a phase-shift network (RC) introduces a 90° phase shift between the horizontal and vertical channels of the oscilloscope that is needed to produce a circle (ring) pattern with the known frequency f_v. Voltage from the unknown frequency source modulates this ring, as shown in Fig. 6-3B. When the voltages across the capacitor and resistor are not equal, the pattern is elliptical, instead of circular, as shown in Fig. 6-3C. The unknown frequency must be higher than the known frequency, and the amplitude of the unknown must be reduced below that of the known to prevent distortion of the pattern. For the required voltages across R and C to be equal the resistance of R must equal the reactance of the 0.1-μfd capacitor C at the frequency of signal source A. Making A variable enables exact setting for a smooth circle.

Measurement Procedure

1. Set up oscilloscope.

2. Switch-off internal sweep.

3. Switch-off sync.

4. Connect equipment as shown in Fig. 6-3A, but temporarily switch-off unknown signal source B.

5. Switch-on signal source A.

6. Adjust R for a ring pattern on screen.

7. Adjust HORIZONTAL and VERTICAL GAIN controls to spread ring over maximum usable area of screen.

8. Switch-on signal source B, noting that ring becomes wrinkled or toothed by unknown signal.

9. Adjust known frequency f_v to stop ring from spinning.

10. Adjust amplitude of f_h voltage for distinct teeth on pattern.

11. Count number (n) of teeth on pattern.

12. Calculate unknown frequency:

$$f_h = nf_v$$

Unless f_h is an integral multiple (even or odd) of f_v, the wheel will spin counterclockwise or clockwise when f_h is not an exact multiple of f_v. Adjust the known frequency to stop the wheel.

6.3 USE OF BROKEN-RING PATTERN

When the oscilloscope has a Z-axis input, a circular pattern may be obtained that is broken into segments (rather than wrinkled) by the unknown signal cycles. Figure 6-4B shows such a pattern (sometimes called *spot wheel* or *dot wheel*). Either the segments or the holes (whichever is more distinct) are counted, and the known frequency is multiplied by this number to determine the unknown frequency. The number of recognizable segments obtained on a circle of given circumference is usually greater than the number of teeth obtained with the modulated-ring method. As in the latter method, the unknown frequency must be higher than the known frequency.

Figure 6-4A shows the equipment setup. The known signal (f_s) from signal source A is applied to the horizontal and vertical channels of the oscilloscope through a 90° phase-shift network, RC. This

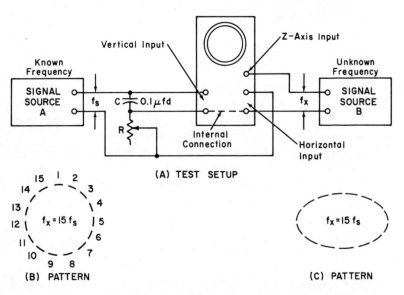

FIG. 6-4. The broken-ring method.

produces a smooth ring pattern on the screen. The unknown signal (f_x) from signal source B is applied to the Z-axis input, and, if of sufficient amplitude, punches a hole in the ring for each negative half-cycle of f_x. The positive half-cycles brighten the segments. The result is the broken-ring pattern shown in Fig. 6-4B.

For a circle pattern, resistance R must equal the reactance of 0.1 µfd capacitor C at frequency f_s. Making R variable enables exact setting of the applied horizontal and vertical voltages for a smooth circle. If the reactances are not equal, the pattern will be elliptical, as in Fig. 6-4C.

Measurement Procedure

1. Set up oscilloscope.

2. Switch-off internal sweep.

3. Switch-off sync.

4. Connect equipment as shown in Fig. 6-4A, but temporarily switch-off unknown signal source B.

5. Switch-on known signal source A.

6. Adjust R for a ring pattern on screen.

7. Adjust HORIZONTAL and VERTICAL GAIN controls to spread ring over maximum usable area of screen.

8. Switch-on signal source B, noting that ring becomes chopped into segments by unknown signal.

9. Adjust known frequency f_s to stop ring from spinning.

10. Adjust amplitude of f_x voltage for clean chopping of ring.

11. Adjust INTENSITY control for sharp contrast between segments and holes in pattern.

12. Count number (n) of segments or holes.

13. Calculate unknown frequency:

$$f_x = nf_s$$

As with the modulated ring, unless f_x is an integral multiple of f_s, the wheel will spin counterclockwise or clockwise when f_x is not an exact multiple of f_s. Adjust the known frequency to stop the spin.

6.4 USE OF BROKEN-LINE PATTERN

A variation of the previous method gives a straight-line trace broken into segments by the unknown frequency. This scheme is simpler, since it requires no phase-shift network, but it does not permit as high a count as the modulated-ring and broken-ring patterns.

In this method, the known frequency (f_s) is applied to the horizontal channel of the oscilloscope and produces a straight, horizontal line trace. The unknown frequency (f_x) is applied to the Z-axis input and, if of sufficient amplitude, punches a hole in the line for each negative half-cycle of f_x. The positive half-cycles brighten the segments. This results in the broken-line pattern shown in Fig. 6-5B.

Measurement Procedure

1. Set up oscilloscope.

2. Switch-off internal sweep.

3. Switch-off sync.

4. Set VERTICAL GAIN control to zero.

5. Connect equipment as shown in Fig. 6-5A, but temporarily switch-off unknown signal source A.

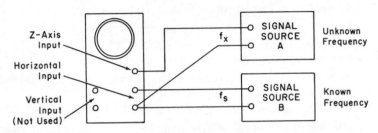

(A) TEST SETUP

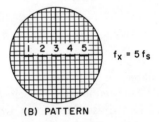

$f_x = 5 f_s$

(B) PATTERN

FIG. 6-5. The broken-line method.

6. Switch-on known signal source B.

7. Adjust HORIZONTAL GAIN control to spread resulting horizontal straight-line trace over maximum usable width of screen.

8. Switch-on signal source A, noting that line becomes broken into segments by unknown signal.

9. Adjust known frequency f_s to stop segments from drifting.

10. Adjust amplitude of f_x voltage for clean segmentation of line.

11. Adjust INTENSITY control for sharp contrast between segments and holes in pattern.

12. Count number (n) of segments.

13. Calculate unknown frequency:

$$f_x = nf_s$$

Unless f_x is an integral multiple of f_s, the segments will drift to the left or to the right when f_x is not an exact multiple of f_s. Adjust the known frequency to freeze the pattern.

6.5 USE OF SAWTOOTH INTERNAL SWEEP

If the SWEEP FREQUENCY controls of the oscilloscope are direct reading in frequency or time, they may be used to identify an unknown frequency.

Measurement Procedure

1. Set up oscilloscope.

2. Switch-on internal sweep.

3. Set SYNC SELECTOR switch to INTERNAL.

4. Connect unknown signal source to VERTICAL INPUT terminals and switch it on.

5. Adjust SWEEP FREQUENCY control(s) and SYNC control for a single, stationary cycle on screen.

6. Adjust HORIZONTAL and VERTICAL GAIN controls for desired width and height of pattern.

7. Read unknown frequency from scale of SWEEP FREQUENCY control(s).

8. If scale is graduated in time units instead of frequency, calculate unknown frequency:

$$f_x = 1/t$$

where t is the time interval (seconds) measured on the screen between the start and end of the cycle.

9. If more than one stationary cycle appears on the screen, count number (n) of cycles, and calculate unknown frequency (f_x) in terms of sweep frequency (f_s):

$$f_x = nf_s$$

Chapter 7

Phase Measurement and Comparison

When its display is properly interpreted, the oscilloscope becomes a convenient and simple phase meter or phase comparator. In this application, the instrument is used much the same as it is for some types of frequency measurement. The oscilloscope appears to be the instrument most widely used for checking phase difference between two signals.

An oscilloscope used for phase measurements must have identical horizontal and vertical amplifiers to insure negligible internal phase shift. Section 7.2 explains how the instrument may be checked for internal shift. High-amplitude signals may be applied directly to the deflecting plates, thus circumventing the amplifiers.

The oscilloscope must also possess excellent linearity and stable beam centering. There should be no interaction between beam centering and signal amplitude.

7.1 USE OF LISSAJOUS FIGURES

When two signals are applied simultaneously to an oscilloscope without internal sweep, one to the horizontal channel and the other to the vertical channel, the resulting pattern is a *Lissajous figure* which shows phase difference between the two signals. Such patterns result from the sweeping of one signal by the other, and are similar to some of the Lissajous figures used for frequency measurement (Section 6.1).

Figure 7-1 shows the test setup for phase measurements by means of Lissajous figures. Figure 7-2 shows patterns corresponding to certain phase difference angles when the two signal voltages are sinusoidal, equal in amplitude, and equal in frequency. Note that the same patterns sometimes are obtained for widely different angles: a right-tilted ellipse for both 45° and 315° (Fig. 7-2B and H). The

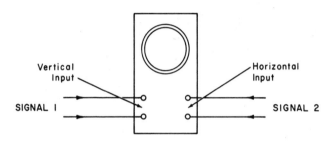

FIG. 7-1. The setup for phase measurement by Lissajous figures.

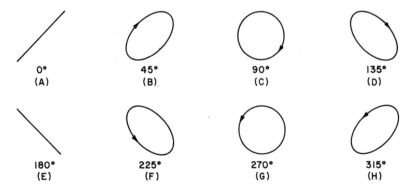

FIG. 7-2. Typical Lissajous figures for phase shift.

spot, however, is moving in a different direction for each: clockwise in Fig. 7-2B and counterclockwise in Fig. 7-2H. The angles shown are for the phase angle of the vertical input with respect to the horizontal input. A simple way to find the correct phase angle (whether leading or lagging) is to introduce a small, known phase shift to one of the inputs. The proper angle may then be deduced by noting the direction in which the pattern changes.

Measurement Procedure

1. Set up oscilloscope.

2. Switch-off internal sweep.

3. Switch-off sync.

4. Apply SIGNAL 1 and SIGNAL 2, as shown in Fig. 7-1.

5. Advance HORIZONTAL and VERTICAL GAIN controls for sample pattern on screen.

6. The two signals should be equal in amplitude. If they are not, either (a) adjust output controls in signal sources for equal signal voltages (with HORIZONTAL and VERTICAL GAIN controls set for identical gain); or (b) if signal sources have no output control, adjust HORIZONTAL and VERTICAL GAIN controls so that equal signal voltages are applied to the deflecting plates.

7. Using the scheme shown in Fig. 7-3A, carefully measure vertical deflection from zero line to point at which pattern intersects center vertical line of screen. Record this dimension (in inches, centimeters, or scale divisions) as A.

8. Carefully measure maximum height of pattern from zero line, and record this dimension as B.

9. Calculate sine of phase difference angle:

$$\sin \theta = A/B$$

10. Find the corresponding angle in a Table of Sines.

It is seen from Fig. 7-3A that this method may be used to find the phase angle from any Lissajous figure obtained by the test method just described. Thus, the ellipse in Fig. 7-3B intersects the vertical axis at 5 divisions and has a maximum height of 6 divisions. From these screen measurements:

$$\sin \theta = 5/6 = 0.8333$$

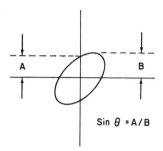

Sin θ = A/B

(A) MEASUREMENTS ON PATTERN

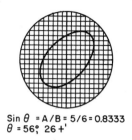

Sin θ = A/B = 5/6 = 0.8333
θ = 56° 26 +'

(B) PATTERN OF TYPICAL
DIMENSIONS

FIG. 7-3. Determination of phase from Lissajous
figures.

A sine table will show that this corresponds to an angle of 56°, 26+'. The straight-line patterns (Fig. 7-2A and 7-2E) intersect the vertical axis at zero, hence A = 0. Their sine, consequently, is equal to 0/B = 0 (corresponding to 0° and 180°, respectively).

7.2 CHECKING INHERENT PHASE SHIFT OF OSCILLOSCOPE

No oscilloscope should be used for phase shift measurements unless its own internal phase shift (the phase difference between horizontal and vertical amplifiers) has been checked first. This difference is held to a small figure in a good oscilloscope having identical horizontal and vertical channels, and, once determined at the frequency to be used in subsequent tests, it may be used to correct test results. If the figure is sizable, however, the oscilloscope should be used for phase measurement with Lissajous figures only when the signals are applied directly to the deflecting plates.

Even an oscilloscope which is suitable in this respect must be checked periodically, since high-order internal phase shift may result from the aging of circuit components.

Figure 7-4 shows the setup for checking internal phase shift. A test signal of desired frequency is applied simultaneously to horizontal and vertical amplifiers. The horizontal and vertical input

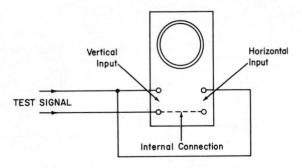

FIG. 7-4. The setup for checking the internal
phase shift of an oscilloscope.

signals are then in phase with each other, since they are the *same*
signal. The resulting Lissajous figure is measured and the phase
angle calculated.

Measurement Procedure

1. Set up oscilloscope.

2. Switch-off internal sweep.

3. Switch-off sync.

4. Apply test signal of desired frequency, as shown in Fig. 7-4.

5. Set HORIZONTAL and VERTICAL GAIN controls for
equal amplification.

6. From Lissajous figure on screen, determine phase angle, as
explained in Section 7.1.

7. Repeat at as many frequencies as practicable throughout
passband of oscilloscope. (Some instruments will show excessive phase shift at some frequencies but will be free of this
trouble at others.)

7.3 USE OF DUAL PATTERN

A dual-trace display offers the advantage that two signal waves
and their phase relations may be observed directly without Lissajous
figures. Neither the signal amplitudes nor frequencies need be equal,
nor need either signal be sinusoidal.

Figure 7-5 illustrates this method. In Fig. 7-5A, an oscilloscope is shown which has two-channel input. Such an instrument might employ a two-gun CRT. In Fig. 7-5B, a conventional oscilloscope is shown with an electronic switch. The latter (see Section 3.10) enables two signals to be displayed simultaneously on the screen on a single-gun CRT. The signal-position control may be adjusted for separated traces (Fig. 7-5C) or superimposed traces (Fig. 7-5D).

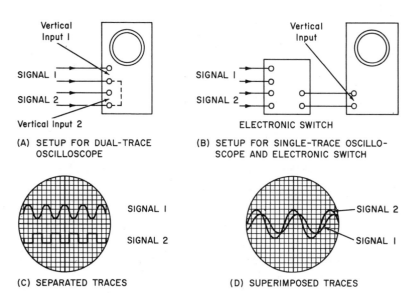

(A) SETUP FOR DUAL-TRACE OSCILLOSCOPE

(B) SETUP FOR SINGLE-TRACE OSCILLOSCOPE AND ELECTRONIC SWITCH

(C) SEPARATED TRACES

(D) SUPERIMPOSED TRACES

FIG. 7-5. The use of a dual pattern.

In most cases, the phase relationships may be determined by inspection. Thus, in Fig. 7-5C, Signal 1 (sine wave) is seen to be 180° out of phase with Signal 2 (square wave), since one reaches its positive peak at the same instant that the other reaches its negative peak. In Fig. 7-5D, Signal 2 is seen to lead Signal 1 by one-eighth of a cycle (45°).

The same technique may be employed to check phase relations of several signals when the oscilloscope or electronic switch provides more than two signal inputs (Tektronix Type 661 oscilloscope with Type M preamplifier, for example, will handle four signals).

Measurement Procedure

1. Set up oscilloscope.

2. Switch-on internal sweep.

3. Set SYNC SELECTOR switch to INTERNAL.

4. Apply test signals to oscilloscope, as shown in Fig. 7-5A or B.

5. Adjust SWEEP FREQUENCY and SYNC controls for several stationary cycles of each signal.

6. Adjust HORIZONTAL and VERTICAL GAIN controls for desired width and height of patterns.

7. Adjust SIGNAL POSITION control (in electronic switch or dual trace oscilloscope) to separate patterns (Fig. 7-5C) or superimpose them (Fig. 7-5D), as desired.

8. Determine phase difference by noting displacement of one signal with respect to the other along horizontal axis.

7.4 CHECKING PHASE ANGLE BETWEEN CURRENT AND VOLTAGE

The preceding sections explained the measurement of phase angle between two voltages. In practice, it is often necessary to measure the angle between voltage and current. In this case, the current may be handled by converting it into a proportional voltage. This is done by passing it through a low, noninductive resistance and using the voltage drop across this resistance as the oscilloscope signal.

Figure 7-6 shows a typical setup. Either a dual-trace oscilloscope or single-trace oscilloscope with electronic switch must be used (see Fig. 7-5). Here, it is desired to know the phase relationship between voltage E_1 across the load and current I through the load. Resistance R is negligible with respect to the load impedance (generally it is between 1 and 10 ohms). Load voltage E_1 is applied to VERTICAL INPUT No. 1 to produce one pattern on the screen. Load current I sets up a voltage drop, E_2, across resistor R, and this voltage is applied to VERTICAL INPUT No. 2 to produce a second pattern, which is proportional to the current. From these two patterns, phase relations may be observed, as in Fig. 7-5C and D.

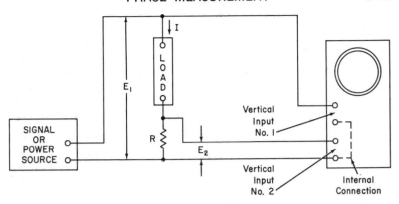

FIG. 7-6. The setup for checking the angle
between current and voltage.

Measurement Procedure

1. Set up oscilloscope.

2. Switch-on internal sweep.

3. Set SYNC SELECTOR switch to INTERNAL.

4. Connect equipment as shown in Fig. 7-6. If dual-trace oscilloscope is not available, use conventional oscilloscope with electronic switch (Fig. 7-5B).

5. Adjust SWEEP FREQUENCY and SYNC controls for several stationary cycles of each pattern.

6. Adjust HORIZONTAL and VERTICAL GAIN controls for desired width and height of pattern.

7. Adjust SIGNAL POSITION control (in electronic switch or dual trace oscilloscope) to separate patterns (Fig. 7-5C) or superimpose them (Fig. 7-5D), as desired.

8. Determine phase difference between current and voltage by noting displacement of one signal with respect to the other along horizontal axis. Use method outlined in Section 7.3.

Current-voltage phase shift may be checked also with Lissajous figures (Section 7.1). The load voltage may be applied to the vertical input, and the voltage drop developed by the load current flowing in a small series resistance may be applied to the horizontal input.

7.5 CHECKING PHASE ANGLE BETWEEN TWO CURRENTS

When the phase angle between two currents is to be checked, the currents are passed through separate low resistances, and the resulting voltage drops are applied to the two vertical inputs of a dual-trace oscilloscope or to the two signal inputs of an electronic switch operated into a conventional oscilloscope. The angle is then determined from the relationship of the two patterns, as explained in Section 7.3.

Figure 7-7 shows the test setup. Current 1 flows through resistor R_1 and sets up voltage drop E_1, which produces one pattern on the screen. Current 2 flows through resistor R_2 and sets up voltage drop E_2, which produces a second pattern. The height of each pattern is proportional to the corresponding current. The resistances are so low (1 ohm, for example) that their presence will not upset operation of the circuit to which the instrument is connected.

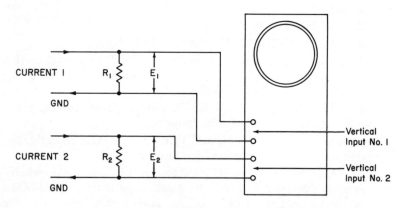

FIG. 7-7. The setup for checking the angle between two currents (common ground).

Measurement Procedure

1. Set up oscilloscope.
2. Switch-on internal sweep.
3. Set SYNC SELECTOR switch to INTERNAL.

4. Connect equipment as shown in Fig. 7-7. If dual-trace oscilloscope is not available, use conventional oscilloscope with electronic switch.

5. Adjust SWEEP FREQUENCY and SYNC controls for several stationary cycles of each pattern. (Sweep and sync are common to both signals.)

6. Adjust HORIZONTAL and VERTICAL GAIN controls for desired width and height of patterns.

7. Adjust SIGNAL POSITION control (in electronic switch or in dual-trace oscilloscope) to separate patterns (Fig. 7-5C) or superimpose them (Fig. 7-5D), as desired.

8. Determine phase difference angle between two currents by noting displacement of one pattern with respect to the other along horizontal axis. Use method outlined in Section 7.3.

7.6 SIMULTANEOUS MEASUREMENT OF VOLTAGE (OR CURRENT) AND PHASE

When using the dual (or multiple) trace method (Sections 7.3, 7.4, 7.5), the signal patterns may be checked for voltage, as well as for phase. Voltage may be measured from the direct screen calibration (Section 5.2) or by use of a voltage calibrator (Section 5.3). If an electronic switch is used, the voltage measurement must be corrected for any error introduced by that device.

Current may be determined by (a) measuring the voltage (for example, E_1 in Fig. 7-7); and (b) calculating current in terms of this voltage and the shunt resistance (for example, R_1 in Fig. 7-7): $I = E_1/R_1$, where I is in amperes, E_1 in volts, and R_1 in ohms.

Chapter 8

A-F Amplifier Tests and Measurements

Engineer, laboratory aide, service technician, and audiophile alike find the oscilloscope a serviceable audio tool. Use of this single instrument can be informative, as well as a time and labor saver in design checking, trouble-shooting, and maintenance.

The oscilloscope used to check modern audio-frequency equipment should have reasonably good frequency response (up to at least 500 kc for the vertical channel). The reason for this bandpass requirement is that high-fidelity gear often is rated up to 50 or 100 kc, and test equipment should be capable of passing harmonics of the higher frequencies. Also, there is the possibility that audio laboratory work will include supersonics.

This chapter outlines the principal a-f test procedures. The number of applications may be expanded considerably from the mere consideration that the oscilloscope is essentially an electronic a-c voltmeter that also supplies a waveform display.

8.1 CHECKING WAVE SHAPE

The oscilloscope can quickly verify the waveform of an a-f signal (whether it is sinusoidal or rectangular, sawtooth or steep pulse, pure or distorted, etc.). The instrument is often used to obtain a qualitative indication of this sort when type of wave—not frequency, voltage, or phase—is the chief matter of interest. It often is used directly to inspect the signal present in an amplifier or line, or delivered by a generator or a playback head. It is also used in conjunction with some other instrument, such as a voltmeter, current meter, distortion meter, or wave analyzer, to monitor waveform while the other instrument indicates a quantity.

Test Procedure

1. Set up oscilloscope.

2. Switch-on internal sweep.

3. Set SYNC SELECTOR switch to INTERNAL.

4. Connect VERTICAL INPUT terminals to signal source. Use low-capacitance probe if minimum disturbance to source must be assured.

5. Adjust SWEEP FREQUENCY and SYNC controls for several stationary cycles on screen.

6. Adjust HORIZONTAL and VERTICAL GAIN controls for desired width and height of pattern.

7. Observe shape of signal pattern. For checking voltage, see Chapter 5; for frequency, see Chapter 6; for distortion, see Section 8.7.

8.2 CHECKING VOLTAGE GAIN OR LOSS

In this application, the oscilloscope is used as a high-impedance electronic a-f voltmeter. Its sensitivity in the millivolts region depends upon the gain (sensitivity) of the vertical amplifier. Figure 8-1 shows the test setup. Here, the *a-f unit* may be a complete amplifier, one or more stages of an amplifier, a component (such as a transformer), or a network (such as a filter). The signal generator is a low-distortion source set to the desired test frequency.

Measurement Procedure

1. Set up oscilloscope.

2. Switch-on internal sweep.

3. Set SYNC SELECTOR switch to INTERNAL.

4. Connect probe to high VERTICAL INPUT terminal.

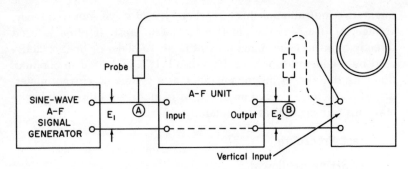

FIG. 8-1. The setup for checking voltage gain.

5. Set up equipment as shown in Fig. 8-1, and switch-on generator and a-f unit.

6. If a-f unit is amplifier, set its gain and tone controls to desired operating point.

7. Connect probe to point B.

8. Increase generator output until pattern appears on screen.

9. Adjust SWEEP FREQUENCY and SYNC controls for several stationary cycles on screen.

10. Adjust HORIZONTAL and VERTICAL GAIN controls for desired width and height of pattern.

11. If a-f unit is overdriven, as evidenced by flattening of signal peaks, reduce output of signal generator to remove this distortion.

12. Transfer probe to point A.

13. From pattern on screen, measure voltage (E_1) at this point, using one of voltage-measurement methods given in Chapter 5.

14. Transfer probe to point B.

15. From pattern on screen measure voltage (E_2) at this point.

16. Calculate voltage gain:

$$A = E_2/E_1$$

Expressed in decibels, $A = 20 \log_{10} E_2/E_1$.

8.3 CHECKING FREQUENCY RESPONSE

This application demands that the oscilloscope response be excellent up to at least twice the highest test frequency to be used. The test method is simple. A constant-amplitude, sinusoidal, test-signal voltage is applied to the amplifier or component under test. The signal frequency is varied throughout the a-f spectrum (e. g., 20 to 25,000 cps) and the corresponding amplifier output voltages are checked at as many frequencies as practicable. The oscilloscope is used to check the input and output voltages, and a curve may be drawn to show variation of output voltage with frequency (Fig. 8-2).

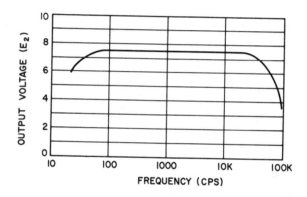

FIG. 8-2. A typical frequency response curve.

Test Procedure

1. Set up oscilloscope.
2. Switch-on internal sweep.
3. Set SYNC SELECTOR switch to INTERNAL.
4. Connect probe to high VERTICAL INPUT terminal.
5. Set up equipment as shown in Fig. 8-1, and switch-on.
6. If a-f unit is power amplifier, connect load resistor to its output terminals. Load resistance must equal normal load impedance of amplifier. Set gain and tone controls of amplifier to desired operating position.

7. Connect probe to point B.

8. Set generator to lowest test frequency.

9. Adjust generator output until pattern appears on screen.

10. Adjust SWEEP FREQUENCY and SYNC controls for several stationary cycles on screen.

11. Adjust HORIZONTAL and VERTICAL GAIN controls for desired width and height of pattern.

12. If a-f unit is overdriven, as evidenced by flattening of signal peaks, reduce generator output to remove this distortion.

13. Transfer probe to point A.

14. From pattern on screen, measure input voltage (E_1) at this point, using one of voltage-measurement methods given in Chapter 5. This is the value of input voltage which must be maintained throughout test.

15. Transfer probe to point B.

16. From pattern on screen, measure output voltage (E_2) at this point and record this value.

17. At each new test frequency, first set E_1 to its initial value, then measure and record output voltage E_2.

18. From these output-voltage data, draw a response curve similar to Fig. 8-2.

A separate frequency response check should be made with the tone control of the amplifier in each of its positions.

8.4 CHECKING HUM AND NOISE LEVEL

Measurement of residual hum and noise in an amplifier, under zero-signal conditions, requires a sensitive oscilloscope. This is because of the low amplitude of hum and noise voltages (often less than 1 millivolt rms). The proper procedure is to check the output of the amplifier, with power switched on but with no input signal. Any output voltage under these conditions will be due to hum, noise, or self-oscillation. Use of the oscilloscope has the advantage that waveform, as well as voltage amplitude, may be observed, and the components may be identified by means of frequency measurements.

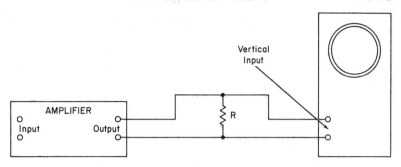

FIG. 8-3. The setup for the hum and noise test.

Test Procedure

1. Set up oscilloscope.

2. Switch-on internal sweep.

3. Set SYNC SELECTOR switch to INTERNAL.

4. Set up equipment as shown in Fig. 8-3. Use shortest possible leads between amplifier and oscilloscope. If unit under test is a power amplifier, terminate it with a resistance (R) equal to the normal load impedance of the amplifier.

5. Switch-on amplifier and set its gain control to zero.

6. Adjust VERTICAL GAIN control until hash pattern appears on screen.

7. Adjust SWEEP FREQUENCY and HORIZONTAL GAIN controls to spread pattern to desired width.

8. Measure signal voltage, using one of the methods outlined in Chapter 5. This is the total voltage due to hum and noise.

9. To separate hum component for observation and measurement, set SWEEP FREQUENCY control to power-line frequency, and set SYNC control for one stationary cycle on screen.

10. If oscillation is present, identify its frequency by one of the methods outlined in Chapter 6.

11. Repeat all tests with amplifier gain control set to maximum.

8.5 MEASURING POWER OUTPUT

This is another application in which the oscilloscope is used essentially as an electronic a-f voltmeter. Figure 8-4 shows the test setup.

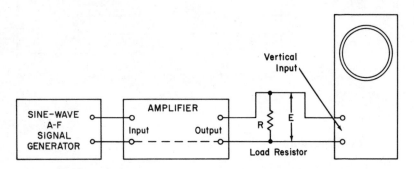

FIG. 8-4. The setup for power output measurement.

Measurement Procedure

1. Set up oscilloscope.

2. Switch-on internal sweep.

3. Set SYNC SELECTOR switch to INTERNAL.

4. Set up equipment as shown in Fig. 8-4. Resistance R must equal the normal load impedance of amplifier.

5. Switch-on amplifier and generator, and set amplifier gain control to maximum-gain position. Set generator to desired test frequency.

6. Advance output of generator.

7. Adjust VERTICAL GAIN control until pattern appears on screen.

8. Adjust SWEEP FREQUENCY and SYNC controls for several stationary cycles.

9. If amplifier is overdriven, as evidenced by flattening of signal peaks, reduce generator output to remove this distortion.

10. Measure rms signal voltage (E_1), using one of methods outlined in Chapter 5.

11. Calculate power output:

$$P = E^2/R$$

where P is in watts, E in volts, and R in ohms.

12. Repeat power measurement at each desired test frequency within passband of amplifier.

8.6 CHECKING PHASE SHIFT

The phase shift introduced by a complete amplifier or by a single amplifier stage (or combination of stages) may be measured with the setup shown in Fig. 8-5.

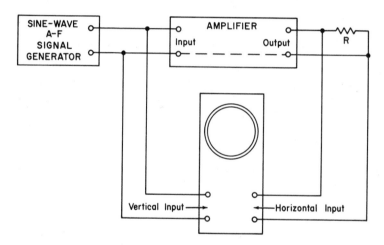

FIG. 8-5. The setup for phase-shift measurement.

Measurement Procedure

1. Set up oscilloscope.

2. Switch-off internal sweep.

3. Switch-off sync.

4. Set up equipment as shown in Fig. 8-5, using shortest possible leads between oscilloscope and amplifier. Resistor R is required only when unit under test is power amplifier, and then resistance must equal normal load impedance of amplifier.

5. Set generator to desired test frequency, and switch-on generator and amplifier.

6. Set amplifier gain and tone controls to desired operating position.

7. Advance generator output for undistorted operation of amplifier.

8. Set HORIZONTAL and VERTICAL GAIN controls for equal horizontal and vertical gain.

9. From Lissajous figure on screen (similar to Fig. 7-2), use the method explained in Section 7.1 to determine phase shift.

10. Repeat phase measurement at several frequencies in passband of amplifier and at several settings of amplifier gain control.

Phase shift may also be checked with a dual-trace oscilloscope (or single-trace oscilloscope with electronic switch). The input of the amplifier in Fig. 8-5 would then be connected to one vertical input; the output of the amplifier would be connected to the other vertical input. Phase would be checked from the dual pattern by the method explained in Section 7.3.

8.7 CHECKING DISTORTION

The oscilloscope may be used in several ways to check harmonic distortion. Some tests are purely qualitative (they serve only to show *presence* of distortion). Others are quantitative; they are concerned not only with presence, but amount of distortion. In either case, the oscilloscope must have low-distortion horizontal and vertical channels. Several tests are described in the following paragraphs.

Sine-Wave Patterns. The simplest qualitative test of distortion is made by (a) applying a low-distortion sine-wave test signal to the amplifier; (b) observing the output with an oscilloscope connected to the amplifier output terminals; and (c) noting the deviation of the output waveform from true sinusoidal. If the distortion is appreciable, the disfigurement of the pattern may quickly be spotted by eye. Generator distortion may be observed in the same way when the oscilloscope is connected directly to the generator output.

Figure 8-6 shows some of the distortion patterns obtained in this type of test. Those in Fig. 8-6A, B, C, J, K, and L are distorted sine waves reproduced with the internal sweep switched-on. Those in Fig. 8-6D, E, F, G, H, and I are distorted Lissajous phase-shift figures obtained when the oscilloscope is operated in the manner explained in Section 6.1.

Each of these patterns represents severe distortion. Slight distortion is not so apparent and usually is spotted only through measurements made on the screen. However, some experienced technicians claim that they are able to detect total distortion as low as 5 percent by visual inspection of a pattern.

The harmonic content of a displayed pattern may be appraised with fair accuracy by computing the amplitude of each principal harmonic by means of a simplified Fourier analysis of the wave. This technique is beyond the scope of this book.

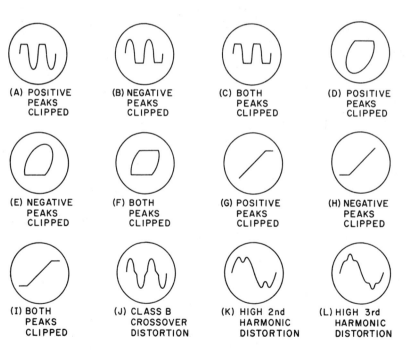

(A) POSITIVE PEAKS CLIPPED

(B) NEGATIVE PEAKS CLIPPED

(C) BOTH PEAKS CLIPPED

(D) POSITIVE PEAKS CLIPPED

(E) NEGATIVE PEAKS CLIPPED

(F) BOTH PEAKS CLIPPED

(G) POSITIVE PEAKS CLIPPED

(H) NEGATIVE PEAKS CLIPPED

(I) BOTH PEAKS CLIPPED

(J) CLASS B CROSSOVER DISTORTION

(K) HIGH 2nd HARMONIC DISTORTION

(L) HIGH 3rd HARMONIC DISTORTION

FIG. 8-6. Simple distortion patterns.

When using a dual-trace oscilloscope (or single-trace oscilloscope with electronic switch), the input and output signals of an amplifier under test may be positioned closely on the screen for comparison of waveform. Allowance must be made, however, for any distortion in the electronic switch.

Use of Fundamental Suppressor. Several distortion meters operate by removing the fundamental frequency of a low-distortion test signal from the amplifier output and indicating the amplitude of the remaining voltage. If this latter voltage is due to harmonics produced by distortion in the amplifier, as it is assumed to be, the distortion percentage is indicated by the ratio of the total harmonic voltage to the amplifier output voltage containing fundamental and harmonics.

Several circuits have been designed for this type of measurement. Figure 8-7 shows the basic elements of one of these. Here, the fundamental suppressor is a bridged-T network (L-C_1-C_2-R_s). Inductance L and identical capacitances C_1 and C_2 are chosen for null at the desired test frequency fundamental (f):

$$C_1 = C_2 = 1/(19.75 \ f^2 \ L)$$

where C is in farads, f in cps, and L in henries. The Q of the inductor should be 10 or higher. Adjustment of the rheostat, R_s, deepens the null. The required resistance at null is inversely proportional to the equivalent series resistance of inductor L.

The amplifier is driven by a low-distortion sine-wave signal generator, and, if a power amplifier, is terminated with a resistance R_L equal to its load impedance. Switch S is thrown first to position 1, and the entire output voltage (E_1) of the amplifier is measured with the oscilloscope. S then is thrown to position 2, rheostat R_s is adjusted for null, and the harmonic voltage (E_2) is measured. Distortion percentage is then calculated:

$$D(\%) = 100(E_2/E_1).$$

Measurement Procedure

1. Set up oscilloscope.
2. Switch-on internal sweep.
3. Set SYNC SELECTOR switch to INTERNAL.
4. Set up equipment as shown in Fig. 8-7.

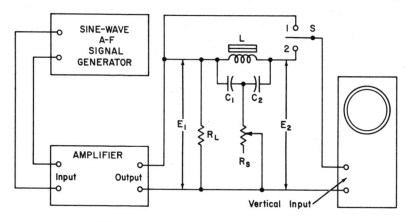

FIG. 8-7. The setup for harmonic distortion measurement.

5. Switch-on amplifier and set its gain and tone controls to desired operating point.

6. Switch-on generator and set it to null frequency of bridged-T network. Adjust generator output for normal power output (or voltage output) of amplifier.

7. Set switch S to position 1.

8. Adjust VERTICAL GAIN control until pattern appears on screen.

9. Adjust SWEEP FREQUENCY, HORIZONTAL GAIN, and SYNC controls for several stationary cycles on screen.

10. From this pattern, measure voltage E_1, using one of methods outlined in Chapter 5.

11. Throw switch S to position 2, adjust R_s for deepest null, and record the voltage at null as E_2.

12. Calculate total harmonic distortion:

$$D(\%) = 100(E_2/E_1)$$

13. Repeat distortion measurement at several settings of amplifier gain control and at several test frequencies (C_1 and C_2 must be changed for a new frequency).

A sensitive, accurately calibrated oscilloscope is superior to a v-t voltmeter in this application, since the oscilloscope shows the waveform as well as the amplitude of the harmonic voltage. The meter can give erroneous indications when it has been calibrated on a sine-wave basis and the distortion voltage is nonsinusoidal.

Oscilloscope with Tunable Distortion Meter. Another fundamental suppression type of distortion meter employs a tunable RC network continuously to vary the null frequency. This avoids the single-frequency inconvenience of the bridged-T filter shown in Fig. 8-7. This type of instrument has a meter reading directly in distortion percentage, but it also has an output jack or terminals for connection of an oscilloscope to monitor the harmonic waveform.

8.8 CHECKING INTERMODULATION

To check intermodulation, a mixed signal (consisting of a low and a high frequency) is applied to the input of the amplifier under test. If there is intermodulation in the amplifier, the output signal of the amplifier will be amplitude modulated (the higher-frequency signal modulated by the lower-frequency one). From the a-m waveform displayed on the oscilloscope screen, the intermodulation percentage may be determined.

Figure 8-8A shows a test setup for intermodulation measurement. The generator supplies a mixed signal, such as 60 and 7000 cps. The

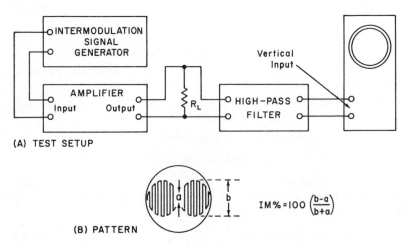

(A) TEST SETUP

(B) PATTERN

$$IM\% = 100 \left(\frac{b-a}{b+a}\right)$$

FIG. 8-8. The setup for intermodulation measurement.

amplifier is terminated by a resistor R_L that is equal to its normal load impedance. The high-pass filter transmits the modulated high-frequency signal, but blocks the low-frequency signal. The a-m wave is displayed on the oscilloscope screen and resembles Fig. 8-8B.

Measurement Procedure

1. Set up oscilloscope.

2. Switch-on internal sweep.

3. Set SYNC SELECTOR switch to INTERNAL.

4. Set up equipment as shown in Fig. 8-8A.

5. Switch-on amplifier and set its gain and tone controls to desired operating point.

6. Switch-on generator and adjust its output for normal power output of amplifier.

7. Adjust VERTICAL GAIN control until pattern appears on screen.

8. Adjust SWEEP FREQUENCY and SYNC controls for several stationary cycles on screen (see Fig. 8-8B).

9. Adjust HORIZONTAL and VERTICAL GAIN controls for desired width and height of pattern.

10. Measure vertical dimensions a and b (see Fig. 8-8B) in screen divisions.

11. Calculate intermodulation percentage:

$$IM(\%) = 100[(b-a)/(b+a)]$$

12. Repeat intermodulation measurement at several settings of gain and tone controls of amplifier.

8.9 SQUARE-WAVE TESTING

The manner in which an amplifier or component handles a square-wave test signal gives a concise estimate of its performance at a number of sine-wave frequencies. A good square wave is applied to the amplifier input, and the output signal is viewed with an oscilloscope. The degree to which the square wave is deformed in passing through the amplifier reveals certain defects in performance; if squareness is preserved, frequency and phase response of the amplifier are good up to approximately 9 times the square-wave frequency. The square wave has high odd-harmonic content. Thus, the 3rd, 5th, 7th, and 9th harmonics are emphasized.

The square-wave generator used in this test should deliver a signal having excellent waveform: flat top, fast rise, fast fall, and negligible overshoot. The oscilloscope channels must themselves have excellent square-wave response. Figure 8-9 shows the test setup.

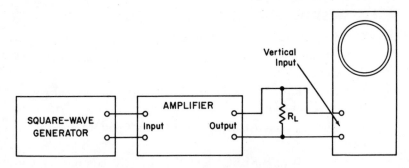

FIG. 8-9. The setup for square-wave testing.

Figure 8-10 shows some of the output square-wave patterns and their interpretations. It is evident from these that degraded low-frequency response tends to round the leading edge of the wave (Fig. 8-10A), whereas degraded high-frequency response rounds the trailing edge (Fig. 8-10G).

Test Procedure

1. Set up oscilloscope.

2. Switch-on internal sweep.

3. Set SYNC SELECTOR switch to INTERNAL.

4. If unit under test is power amplifier, terminate it with load resistance R_L equal to load impedance of amplifier.

5. Set up equipment as shown in Fig. 8-9.

6. Switch-on amplifier and set its gain control and tone control to desired operating point.

7. Switch-on generator and increase its output for peak-to-peak square-wave amplitude not higher than the peak-to-peak voltage that will overdrive amplifier.

8. Adjust VERTICAL GAIN control until pattern appears on screen.

9. Adjust SWEEP FREQUENCY and SYNC controls for one stationary square-wave cycle on screen.

10. Adjust HORIZONTAL and VERTICAL GAIN controls for desired width and height of pattern.

11. Note squareness of pattern, comparing it with samples given in Fig. 8-10 for possible interpretation.

12. Repeat test at several square-wave frequencies and at several settings of the amplifier gain and tone controls.

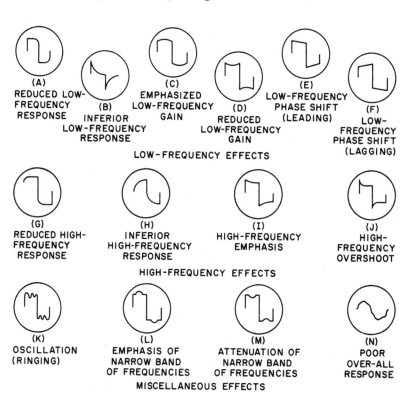

(A)
REDUCED LOW-
FREQUENCY
RESPONSE

(B)
INFERIOR
LOW-FREQUENCY
RESPONSE

(C)
EMPHASIZED
LOW-FREQUENCY
GAIN

(D)
REDUCED
LOW-FREQUENCY
GAIN

(E)
LOW-FREQUENCY
PHASE SHIFT
(LEADING)

(F)
LOW-
FREQUENCY
PHASE SHIFT
(LAGGING)

LOW-FREQUENCY EFFECTS

(G)
REDUCED HIGH-
FREQUENCY
RESPONSE

(H)
INFERIOR
HIGH-FREQUENCY
RESPONSE

(I)
HIGH-FREQUENCY
EMPHASIS

(J)
HIGH-
FREQUENCY
OVERSHOOT

HIGH-FREQUENCY EFFECTS

(K)
OSCILLATION
(RINGING)

(L)
EMPHASIS OF
NARROW BAND
OF FREQUENCIES

(M)
ATTENUATION OF
NARROW BAND
OF FREQUENCIES

(N)
POOR
OVER-ALL
RESPONSE

MISCELLANEOUS EFFECTS

FIG. 8-10. Square-wave test patterns.

8.10 OSCILLOSCOPE AS A-F SIGNAL TRACER

The oscilloscope is superior to the v-t voltmeter as a high-impedance signal tracer in a-f troubleshooting since it will not only show the presence and amplitude of the signal at a test point, but will also reveal its waveform. The oscilloscope will also reveal oscillation, hum, and noise, and will indicate distortion of the signal.

In this application, the oscilloscope is employed in the manner of a voltmeter. When tracing a signal, use a low-capacitance probe, and follow either of the voltage-measuring methods outlined in Chapter 5. Supply a low-distortion, sine-wave test signal to the amplifier (or circuit) input terminals, and move the oscilloscope probe from stage to stage, progressing from input to output, to check presence and amplitude of signal. The amplifier must be in operation and its gain and tone controls set for normal response. A 1000-cps signal is preferable in most cases.

Chapter 9

Receiver Tests and Adjustments

Since its invention, the oscilloscope has been invaluable for testing and adjusting receivers. With radio receivers many adjustments are speeded and refined through use of the oscilloscope; with television receivers *most* adjustments can be made only with the greatest difficulty, if at all, without an oscilloscope. This does not mean that the oscilloscope will replace all other instruments. It is no match for the test meter, for example, in routine checking of current, voltage, resistance, and continuity. Nor will it replace the tube tester. But in such applications as alignment, rapid checking of bandwidth, and checking of TV waveforms, the oscilloscope is almost indispensable.

The service technician who familiarizes himself with oscilloscope techniques in receiver testing will find this instrument to be of constant service not only for the jobs it alone can do, but also as an adjunct to other test equipment. This chapter describes the principal uses of the oscilloscope in this area. Since the examples are intended to be illustrative, typical applications have been chosen. The many variations cannot possibly be touched in a book of this scope. For detailed special procedures, especially for color TV, refer to the set manufacturer's instruction manual.

9.1 VISUAL ALIGNMENT OF AM I-F AMPLIFIER

Figure 9-1A shows the test setup for alignment of the i-f channel of an AM receiver. The sweep generator supplies the intermediate frequency (usually 455 kc) and sweeps this signal by a selected amount above and below center frequency. The sweep generator also supplies a 60-cps sweep signal for the oscilloscope. The marker generator places a pip on the oscilloscope display for frequency identification.

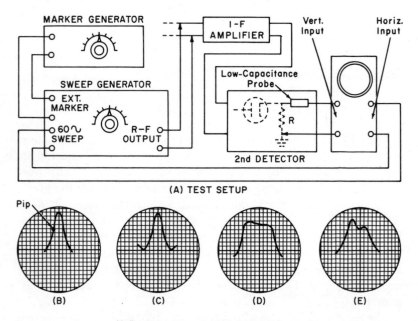

FIG. 9-1. Visual AM i-f alignment.

Test Procedure

1. Set up oscilloscope, with low-capacitance probe.
2. Switch-off internal sweep.
3. Set SYNC SELECTOR switch to EXTERNAL.

4. Set up equipment as shown in Fig. 9-1A:

   (a) Connect sweep generator to input of i-f amplifier.

   (b) External marker generator will not be required if sweep generator has internal variable-frequency marker.

   (c) Connect VERTICAL INPUT (probe) to 2nd detector load resistor, R, in receiver.

   (d) Connect HORIZONTAL INPUT terminals to 60-cps output of sweep generator.

5. Switch-on receiver and generators, reduce output of generators temporarily to zero, and detune receiver from any strong station.

6. Set sweep generator output to trial level.

7. Tune sweep generator to intermediate frequency (generally 455 kc).

8. Adjust sweep to 30 kc.

9. Adjust VERTICAL GAIN control until pattern appears on screen.

10. Increase sweep generator output, if necessary, to give pattern resembling Fig. 9-1B.

11. Adjust HORIZONTAL and VERTICAL GAIN controls for desired width and height of pattern.

12. If pattern is upside-down, adjust PHASING control in sweep generator to right it.

13. Adjust i-f trimmers for narrow, single-line pattern of type shown in Fig. 9-1B. If sweep generator output is excessive, feet of pattern may tilt upward, as in Fig. 9-1C, or pattern may become double-peaked, as in Fig. 9-1E.

14. When trimmer adjustment is staggered, broad curve (Fig. 9-1D) will be obtained; severe staggering gives double-peak curve (Fig. 9-1E).

15. To check frequency points on curve, advance marker generator output. Note that a pip is produced on curve. Keep marker generator output low, or oversized pip will distort response curve. Tune marker generator, noting that pip moves along curve. The frequency at any desired point on curve, marked by pip, may be read from marker generator dial. In this way, bandwidth of i-f channel may be determined, or trimmers may be set for a desired bandwidth (e. g., flat-top response for high-fidelity service).

9.2 VISUAL ALIGNMENT OF AM FRONT END

The setup for alignment of the front-end (r-f amplifier and 1st detector) stages of an AM receiver is shown in Fig. 9-2. In this arrangement, the center frequency of the sweep generator is selected equal to some desired frequency within the tuning range of the receiver.

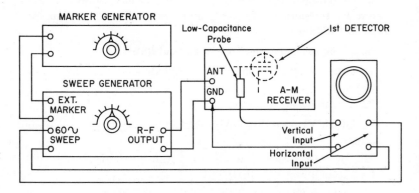

FIG. 9-2. The setup for AM front-end alignment.

Test Procedure

1. Set up oscilloscope, with low-capacitance probe.

2. Switch-off internal sweep.

3. Set SYNC SELECTOR switch to EXTERNAL.

4. Set up equipment as shown in Fig. 9-2:

(a) Connect sweep generator to receiver ANTENNA and GROUND terminals.

(b) External marker generator will not be required if sweep generator has internal variable-frequency marker.

(c) Connect VERTICAL INPUT (probe) to grid of 1st detector (mixer) tube (or to base of transistor in transistorized receiver).

(d) Connect HORIZONTAL INPUT terminals to 60-cps output of sweep generator.

5. Switch-on receiver and generators, and temporarily reduce output of generators to zero.

6. Set sweep generator output to trial level.

7. Tune sweep generator to desired alignment frequency.

8. Tune receiver to center frequency of sweep generator.

9. Adjust sweep to 30 kc.

10. Adjust VERTICAL GAIN control until pattern appears on screen.

11. Increase sweep generator output, if necessary, to give pattern resembling Fig. 9-1B.

12. Adjust HORIZONTAL and VERTICAL GAIN controls for desired width and height of pattern.

13. If pattern is upside-down, adjust PHASE control in sweep generator to right it.

14. Adjust r-f amplifier and 1st detector trimmers for narrow, single-line pattern of type shown in Fig. 9-1B. If sweep generator output is excessive, feet of pattern may tilt upward, as in Fig. 9-1C, or pattern may become double-peaked, as in Fig. 9-1E.

15. When trimmer adjustment is staggered, broad curve (Fig. 9-1D) is obtained; severe staggering gives double-peak curve (Fig. 9-1E).

16. To check frequency points on curve, advance marker generator output. Note that a pip is produced on curve. Keep marker generator output low, or oversized pip will distort response curve. Tune marker generator, noting that pip moves along curve. The frequency of any desired point on curve, marked by pip, may be read from marker generator dial. In this way, r-f bandwidth may be determined, or trimmers may be set for a desired bandwidth (e. g., flat-top response for high-fidelity service).

17. To align oscillator of front end:
    (a) Leave receiver tuned to sweep generator center frequency.
    (b) Reduce marker output to zero.
    (c) Transfer VERTICAL INPUT (probe) to first stage of previously aligned i-f amplifier.
    (d) Adjust oscillator trimmer for pattern resembling Fig. 1-9B.

9.3 VISUAL ALIGNMENT OF FM DETECTOR

Figure 9-3A shows the test setup for alignment of an FM 2nd detector (discriminator or ratio detector). The sweep generator supplies the intermediate frequency (usually 10.7 mc) as the center frequency, and sweeps this signal above and below center by a selected number of kilocycles. The sweep generator also supplies a 60-cps sweep signal for the oscilloscope. The marker generator places a pip on the display for identification of frequency.

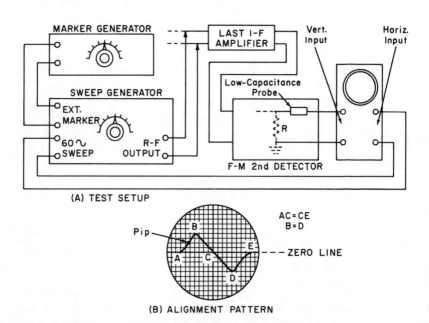

(A) TEST SETUP

(B) ALIGNMENT PATTERN

FIG. 9-3. FM detector alignment.

Test Procedure

1. Set up oscilloscope, with low-capacitance probe.

2. Switch-off internal sweep.

3. Set SYNC SELECTOR switch to EXTERNAL.

4. Set up equipment as shown in Fig. 9-3:

(a) Connect sweep generator to input of last i-f amplifier stage in FM receiver.

(b) External marker generator will not be required if sweep generator has internal variable-frequency marker.

(c) Connect VERTICAL INPUT (probe) to top of load resistor of ratio detector or discriminator (in a discriminator stage, this means the top of the *ungrounded* resistor).

(d) Connect HORIZONTAL INPUT terminals to 60-cps output of sweep generator.

5. Switch-on receiver and generators, and temporarily reduce output of generators to zero.

6. Set sweep generator output to trial level.

7. Tune sweep generator to receiver intermediate frequency (usually 10.7 mc).

8. Adjust sweep to 300 kc.

9. Adjust VERTICAL GAIN control until pattern appears on screen.

10. Increase sweep generator output, if necessary, to give pattern resembling Fig. 9-3B.

11. Adjust HORIZONTAL and VERTICAL GAIN controls for desired width and height of pattern.

12. Adjust trimmers in last i-f and FM detector stages to make pattern correspond to Fig. 9-3B: peaks B and D should be equal in height; points A, C, and E should lie along the zero line.

13. To check frequency points on curve, advance marker generator output. Note that a pip is produced on curve. Keep marker generator output low, or oversized pip will distort curve. Frequency of any desired point on curve, marked by pip, may be read from marker generator dial.

9.4 VISUAL ALIGNMENT OF FM I-F AMPLIFIER

The i-f amplifier of an FM receiver may be aligned in a manner similar to that described for AM i-f alignment in Section 9.1. The test setup is shown in Fig. 9-4.

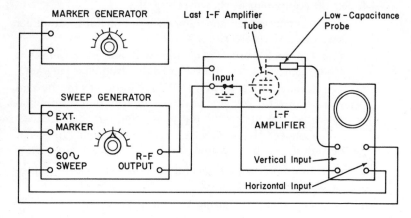

FIG. 9-4. The setup for FM i-f alignment.

Test Procedure

1. Set up oscilloscope, with low-capacitance probe.

2. Switch-off internal sweep.

3. Set SYNC SELECTOR switch to EXTERNAL.

4. Set up equipment as shown in Fig. 9-4:

(a) Connect sweep generator to input i-f amplifier channel; in most sets, this is the grid of 1st detector tube.

(b) External marker generator will not be required if sweep generator has internal variable-frequency marker.

(c) Connect VERTICAL INPUT (probe) to output of i-f amplifier; this is plate of last i-f tube.

(d) Connect HORIZONTAL INPUT terminals to 60-cps output of sweep generator.

5. Switch-on receiver and generators, and reduce output of generators temporarily to zero.

6. Set sweep generator output to trial level.

7. Tune sweep generator to receiver intermediate frequency (usually 10.7 mc).

8. Adjust sweep to 300 kc.

9. Adjust VERTICAL GAIN control until pattern appears on screen.

10. Increase sweep generator output, if necessary, to give pattern resembling Fig. 9-1B.

11. Adjust HORIZONTAL and VERTICAL GAIN controls for desired width and height of pattern.

12. Adjust i-f trimmers for single-line pattern of type shown in Fig. 9-1B. This pattern is i-f response curve. If sweep generator output is excessive, feet of pattern may tilt upward, as in Fig. 9-1C, or pattern may become double-peaked, as in Fig. 9-1E.

13. When trimmer adjustment is staggered, broad curve (Fig. 9-1D) is obtained; severe staggering gives double-peaked curve (Fig. 9-1E).

14. If pattern is upside-down, adjust PHASE control in sweep generator to right it.

15. To check frequency points on curve, advance marker generator output, noting that a pip is produced on curve. Keep marker generator output low, or oversized pip will distort curve. Tune marker generator, noting that pip moves along curve. The frequency of any desired point, marked on curve by pip, may be read from marker generator dial. In this way, i-f bandwidth may be determined, or trimmers may be set for a desired bandwidth (e. g., a flat-top a given number of kc wide, for high-fidelity response).

9.5 VISUAL ALIGNMENT OF FM FRONT END

For alignment of the front end of an FM receiver, follow the instructions given for aligning the front end of an AM receiver (Section 9.2), except for these changes:

1. Tune sweep generator and receiver to desired test frequency in receiver range (usually 88-108 mc).

2. Set sweep to 300 kc.

3. Marker generator must be tunable through receiver frequency range. If this is not possible, use external, unmodulated r-f signal generator as marker generator.

9.6 VISUAL ALIGNMENT OF TV I-F AMPLIFIER

For alignment of the video i-f amplifier of a black-and-white television receiver, use the test setup shown in Fig. 9-4. Connect the sweep generator to the video i-f amplifier input (grid of mixer tube or primary of 1st i-f transformer), and connect the VERTICAL IN-PUT (probe) to the video i-f amplifier output (grid of video amplifier).

Test Procedure

1. Set up oscilloscope, with low-capacitance probe.
2. Switch-off internal sweep.
3. Set SYNC SELECTOR switch to EXTERNAL.
4. Set up equipment as shown in Fig. 9-4:
    (a) Connect sweep generator to input of video i-f amplifier(this will be grid of mixer tube or primary of 1st video i-f transformer).
    (b) External marker generator will not be required if sweep generator has internal variable-frequency marker.
    (c) Connect VERTICAL INPUT (probe) to output of video i-f amplifier (this will be the grid of the video amplifier).
    (d) Connect HORIZONTAL INPUT terminals to 60-cps output of sweep generator.
5. Switch-on receiver and generators, tune receiver to unused TV channel, and reduce output of generators temporarily to zero.
6. Set sweep generator output to trial level.
7. Tune sweep generator to center frequency of i-f passband (e. g., 43 mc in the receiver response curve shown in Fig. 9-5).
8. Adjust sweep to 10 mc.
9. Adjust VERTICAL GAIN control until pattern appears on screen.
10. Increase sweep generator output, if necessary, to give pattern resembling Fig. 9-5. To prevent distortion, use lowest output which will give legible pattern.
11. Adjust HORIZONTAL and VERTICAL GAIN controls for desired width and height of pattern.
12. If pattern is upside-down, adjust PHASE control in sweep generator to right it.
13. Adjust i-f trimmers for response curve resembling Fig. 9-5. See set manufacturer's literature for exact shape of curve.
14. Advance output of marker generator and tune to place pip at recommended points, as in Fig. 9-5. (In the sample curve shown here, 41.25 mc marks the position of the sound carrier

element; 45.75 mc marks the video carrier.) Use minimum marker output, to prevent distortion of pattern.

15. I-f amplifier is correctly adjusted when response curve has shape and signal amplitudes corresponding to set manufacturer's recommended curve. Measure the amplitude at each reference point by one of the methods given in Chapter 5. Thus, in Fig. 9-5, position 41.25 mc (sound carrier) represents 2% of total amplitude of pattern; 45.75 mc point is at 40% of total amplitude, etc. The curve is flat-topped to provide ample passband for a clear, crisp picture.

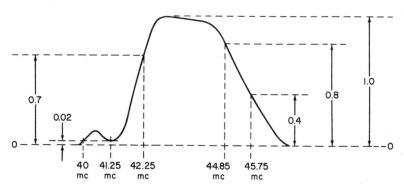

FIG. 9-5. A typical video i-f response pattern.

9.7 VISUAL ALIGNMENT OF TV SOUND I-F AMPLIFIER AND DETECTOR

The 4.5-mc TV sound i-f amplifier and FM detector channel may be aligned in a two-step procedure; first the i-f and then the detector.

Test Procedure

1. Set up oscilloscope, with low-capacitance probe.

2. Switch-off internal sweep.

3. Set SYNC SELECTOR switch to EXTERNAL.

4. Set up equipment as shown in Fig. 9-4:

(a) Connect sweep generator to input of sound i-f amplifier.

(b) External marker generator will not be required if sweep generator has internal variable-frequency marker.

(c) Connect VERTICAL INPUT (probe) to output of sound i-f amplifier.

(d) Connect HORIZONTAL INPUT terminals to 60-cps output of sweep generator.

5. Switch-on receiver and generators, tune receiver to unused TV channel, and reduce output of generators temporarily to zero.

6. Set sweep generator output to trial level.

7. Tune sweep generator to 4.5 mc.

8. Adjust sweep to 300 kc.

9. Adjust VERTICAL GAIN control until pattern appears on screen.

10. Increase sweep generator output, if necessary, to give pattern resembling Fig. 9-1B. This pattern is i-f response curve. If sweep generator output is excessive, feet of pattern may tilt upward, as in Fig. 9-1C, or pattern may become double-peaked, as in Fig. 9-1E.

11. When trimmer adjustment is staggered, broad curve (Fig. 9-1D) is obtained; severe staggering gives double-peaked curve (Fig. 9-1E).

12. If pattern is upside-down, adjust PHASE control in sweep generator to right it.

13. To check frequency points on curve, advance marker generator output, noting that a pip is produced on curve. Keep marker generator output low, or oversized pip will distort curve. Tune marker generator, noting that pip moves along curve. The frequency of any desired point on curve, marked by pip, may be read from marker generator dial. In this way, trimmers may be set for a desired bandwidth, as indicated by set manufacturer's literature.

To align the discriminator or ratio detector of the sound channel, leave the sweep and the marker generator set to the same frequencies as in the preceding i-f alignment, but set up the equipment as shown in Fig. 9-3. Then, follow the instructions given in Section 9.3.

9.8 CHECKING VIDEO AMPLIFIER

The video amplifier is a wideband unit (20 cps to 4.5 mc). Its performance may be rapidly appraised by means of square-wave test signals. For this purpose, the square-wave generator must be tunable from 20 cps to 500 kc, and the oscilloscope must have vertical response to 5 mc or higher and sweep frequency tunable to 500 kc. The test setup is shown in Fig. 9-6.

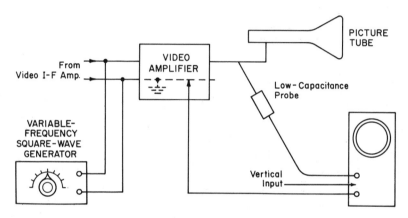

FIG. 9-6. The setup for checking the video amplifier.

Test Procedure

1. Set up oscilloscope with low-capacitance probe.

2. Switch-on internal sweep.

3. Set SYNC SELECTOR switch to INTERNAL.

4. Set up equipment as shown in Fig. 9-6:

(a) Connect square-wave generator to video amplifier input.

(b) Connect VERTICAL INPUT (probe) to video amplifier output.

5. Switch-on receiver and generator, tune receiver to unused TV channel, and reduce generator output temporarily to zero.

6. Set generator output to trial level below overload level of video amplifier (see manufacturer's literature).

7. Tune generator to 20 cps.

8. Adjust VERTICAL GAIN control until pattern appears on screen.

9. Adjust SWEEP FREQUENCY and SYNC controls for single, stationary square-wave cycle on screen. At high frequencies, beyond the maximum sweep frequency, several cycles will appear.

10. Adjust HORIZONTAL and VERTICAL GAIN controls for desired width and height of pattern.

11. Observe pattern for squareness. Compare with sample patterns given in Fig. 8-10.

12. Repeat test at square-wave frequencies of 50 cps, 25 kc, 100 kc, and 500 kc.

13. If CONTRAST control of receiver is in video amplifier, repeat complete test procedure at several settings of this control.

9.9 VISUAL ALIGNMENT OF TV FRONT END

For adjustment of the front end of a TV receiver, follow the instructions given for aligning the front end of an AM receiver (Section 9.2), except for these changes:

1. Tune receiver to desired TV channel frequency.

2. Tune sweep generator to center frequency of that channel.

3. Set sweep to 10 mc.

4. Tune marker first to video carrier and then to sound carrier of channel to which receiver is tuned, and adjust r-f and mixer trimmers for curve of desired bandwidth (as specified by set manufacturer's literature), using marker pips for guidance.

9.10 CHECKING TV OPERATING WAVEFORMS

Video and sync pulse voltages and their operating waveforms should be checked visually for shape. At the same time, their peak amplitudes may be measured on the oscilloscope screen.

For this test, tune-in a TV station, and touch the oscilloscope probe successively to each point of interest in the receiver circuit.

Observe the resulting pattern for shape, measure its peak voltage, and compare these data with the set manufacturer's specifications. For convenience, some oscilloscopes designed for TV work have, in addition to continuously variable sawtooth sweep, two preset sweep frequencies: 7875 cps (which will display two cycles at the TV horizontal frequency) and 30 cps (which will display two cycles at the TV vertical frequency).

Test Procedure

1. Set up oscilloscope. Have low-capacitance probe and demodulator probe available.

2. Switch-on internal sweep.

3. Set SYNC SELECTOR switch to INTERNAL.

4. Connect ground (common) terminal of oscilloscope to chassis or B-minus of receiver.

5. Set receiver to desired channel, and tune-in TV station. Set CONTRAST and HOLD controls of receiver to normal operating point.

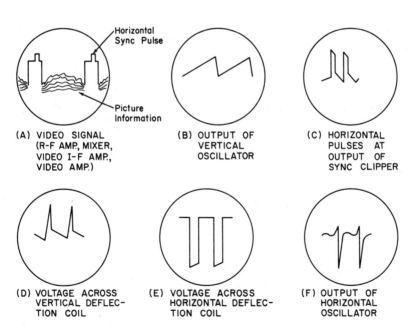

(A) VIDEO SIGNAL
(R-F AMP, MIXER,
VIDEO I-F AMP.,
VIDEO AMP.)

(B) OUTPUT OF
VERTICAL
OSCILLATOR

(C) HORIZONTAL
PULSES AT
OUTPUT OF
SYNC CLIPPER

(D) VOLTAGE ACROSS
VERTICAL DEFLEC-
TION COIL

(E) VOLTAGE ACROSS
HORIZONTAL DEFLEC-
TION COIL

(F) OUTPUT OF
HORIZONTAL
OSCILLATOR

FIG. 9-7. Sample TV operating waveforms.

6. Use demodulator probe when sampling signal in any stage preceding video detector; use low-capacitance probe for signals in and after video detector.

7. Set SWEEP FREQUENCY to 30 cps for vertical signals, or to 7875 cps for horizontal signals.

8. Set SYNC control for two stationary cycles or pulses on screen. Figure 9-7 shows sample signal patterns from an operating TV receiver.

9. Compare shape of signal and its peak-to-peak voltage with set manufacturer's specifications.

9.11 CHECKING RECEIVER AUDIO CHANNEL

To check a-f channel of any AM, FM, or TV receiver, detune receiver from any strong station and check performance as outlined in Sections 8.1 to 8.9.

9.12 OSCILLOSCOPE AS SIGNAL TRACER

The capability of the oscilloscope as an a-f signal tracer was discussed in Section 8.10. This instrument is useful also as an r-f signal tracer in AM, FM, and TV receiver troubleshooting.

A wideband oscilloscope may be used with a low-capacitance probe to trace a signal through all r-f, i-f, and detector stages operating within its frequency range. An a-f type oscilloscope may be used, provided that it is equipped with a demodulator probe and that the AM or FM receiver is operated from a suitably modulated test signal. The TV receiver may be operated from a test pattern generator.

Chapter 10

Transmitter Tests and Adjustments

The adjustment and troubleshooting of a radio transmitter are facilitated by use of a suitable oscilloscope. In some applications, such as modulation checking, the oscilloscope can show more about the nature of the signal and the condition of the transmitter than can an equivalent test meter. In other applications, the oscilloscope is a useful adjunct to listening tests and to meters inside and outside the transmitter.

This chapter describes principal applications of the oscilloscope in radio transmitter testing. Specific tests on television transmitters are not included, since they are beyond the scope of this book.

10.1 CHECKING AMPLITUDE MODULATION BY SINE-WAVE METHOD

This is one of the oldest uses of the oscilloscope in radio transmitter testing. With this method, the AM wave is displayed on the screen, and the modulation percentage is determined from the vertical dimensions of the pattern. Figure 10-1A and B shows the test setup.

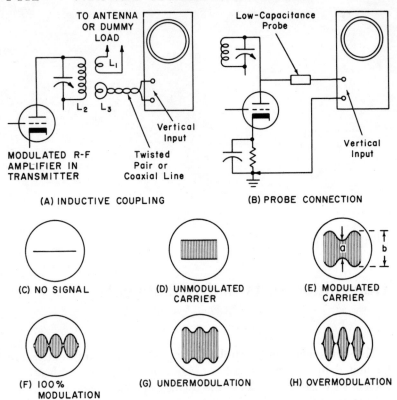

FIG. 10-1. AM checking with sine-wave patterns.

Test Procedure

1. Set up oscilloscope.
2. Switch-on internal sweep.
3. Set SYNC SELECTOR switch to INTERNAL.
4. Set up equipment as shown in Fig. 10A or B:

   (a) If frequency response of vertical amplifier does not reach transmitter carrier frequency, use direct input to vertical deflecting plates through a small 3-turn pickup coil (L_3) coupled to tank of modulated r-f amplifier in transmitter, as shown in Fig. 10-1A. If oscilloscope can handle carrier frequency, vertical amplifier may be used with either inductive coupling (Fig. 10-1A) or low-capacitance probe (Fig. 10-1B). With latter method, combined d-c and r-f voltage in transmitter must not exceed breakdown voltage of probe and oscilloscope.

(b) With transmitter OFF, set VERTICAL GAIN control to trial position.

(c) Set SWEEP FREQUENCY and HORIZONTAL GAIN controls for a single-line trace over most of screen (Fig. 10-1C).

(d) Switch-on *unmodulated* transmitter. Unmodulated carrier gives pattern shown in Fig. 10-1D.

(e) Modulate transmitter with low-distortion, sine-wave audio frequency. Amplitude modulation gives wave pattern similar to Fig. 10-1E, F, G, or H.

(f) Adjust HORIZONTAL and VERTICAL GAIN controls for desired width and height of pattern.

(g) Adjust SWEEP FREQUENCY and SYNC controls for 2 or 3 stationary cycles of pattern on screen.

(h) Measure minimum height a and maximum height b of pattern in number of screen divisions, as shown in Fig. 10-1E.

(i) Calculate modulation percentage:

$$M(\%) = 100[(b-a)/(b+a)]$$

Figure 10-1F shows shape of pattern for a fully modulated wave (M = 100%). Figures 10-1G and H show shapes for undermodulation and overmodulation, respectively.

10.2 CHECKING AMPLITUDE MODULATION WITH TRAPEZOIDAL PATTERNS

This method is somewhat simpler than the one described in Section 10.1 because it does not involve use of the internal sweep of the oscilloscope. It is widely used for direct checking of amplitude modulation and for the calibration of modulation meters. Figure 10-2A shows the test setup.

Test Procedure

1. Set up oscilloscope.

2. Switch-off internal sweep.

3. Set SYNC SELECTOR switch to EXTERNAL.

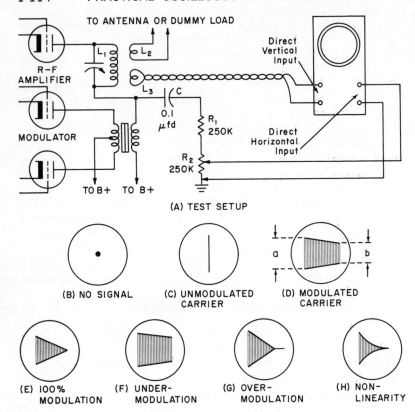

FIG. 10-2. AM checking with trapezoidal patterns.

4. Set up equipment as shown in Fig. 10-2A:

(a) Do not use oscilloscope amplifiers. Couple direct vertical input to tank of modulated r-f amplifier in transmitter through small 3-turn pickup coil L_3. Connect direct horizontal input to output of modulator through voltage divider network C-R_1-R_2.

(b) With transmitter OFF, set HORIZONTAL and VERTICAL GAIN controls to trial position. Single-dot pattern (Fig. 10-2B) appears on screen.

(c) Switch-on *unmodulated* transmitter. Unmodulated carrier gives pattern shown in Fig. 10-2C.

(d) Modulate transmitter with low-distortion, sine-wave audio frequency. Amplitude modulation gives trapezoidal pattern similar to Fig. 10-2D, E, F, G, or H.

(e) Adjust coupling between L_1 and L_3 for height, and R_2 for width, to spread pattern over useful area of screen.

(f) Measure maximum height a and minimum height b of pattern in number of screen divisions, as shown in Fig. 10-2D.

(g) Calculate modulation percentage:

$$M(\%) = 100[(a-b)/(a+b)]$$

Figure 10-2E shows the trapezoid shape for a fully modulated wave ($M = 100\%$). Figures 10-2F and G show shapes for under-modulation and overmodulation, respectively. An advantage of the trapezoidal pattern is its ability to show linearity of the modulated r-f amplifier; the straightness of the sides of the trapezoid indicates this linearity. In Figure 10-2H, the sides are curved, indicating non-linearity.

10.3 CHECKING MODULATOR CHANNEL

The speech amplifier-modulator channel of a transmitter is an a-f system. Its performance may be checked in terms of gain, frequency response, harmonic distortion, phase shift, intermodulation, power output, hum, and noise.

For explanations of how to use the oscilloscope to make these tests, see Sections 8.2 to 8.9.

10.4 CHECKING FREQUENCY-MULTIPLIER OPERATION

In the adjustment of a transmitter, especially a new one, there is a great possibility that an r-f amplifier, doubler, tripler, or quad-rupler may be tuned to the wrong frequency. This can have serious consequences (legal as well as technical).

Because of harmonic response, frequency meters sometimes confuse the operator, leaving him unsure of transmitter adjustments. The oscilloscope is a trustworthy comparator of frequencies. Its use for this purpose at audio frequencies is treated in Chapter 6. The instrument may also be used to compare radio frequencies, and thus may reveal the operating frequency of transmitter stages with respect to the master oscillator frequency.

Figure 10-3 shows a test setup for using Lissajous figures to determine frequency (f_x) of an amplifier or multiplier stage with respect to the frequency (f_1) of the oscillator stage. In this application, direct input to the horizontal and vertical deflecting plates via the shortest possible leads must be used. Figure 10-4 shows the Lissajous figures obtained for f_x:f_1 ratios of 1:1, 2:1, 3:1, and 4:1 (straight-through, doubling, tripling, and quadrupling) at phase difference angles of 0°, 45°, 90°, 135°, and 180°.

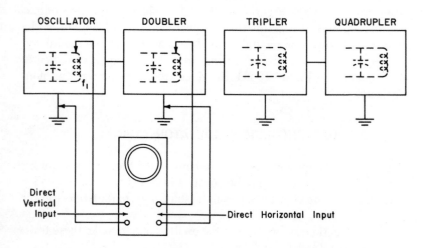

FIG. 10-3. Checking frequency-multiplier operation.

Test Procedure

1. Set up oscilloscope.
2. Switch-off internal sweep.
3. Set SYNC SELECTOR switch to EXTERNAL.
4. Set up equipment as shown in Fig. 10-3:

   (a) Using shortest possible leads, connect direct vertical input to oscillator tank circuit, and connect direct horizontal input to tank circuit of stage under inspection.

(b) Set HORIZONTAL and VERTICAL GAIN controls to zero.

(c) Switch-on transmitter.

(d) Tune transmitter throughout and observe Lissajous figure on screen.

(e) Compare with Fig. 10-4 to determine if stage under inspection is passing oscillator frequency or is doubling, tripling, or quadrupling that frequency.

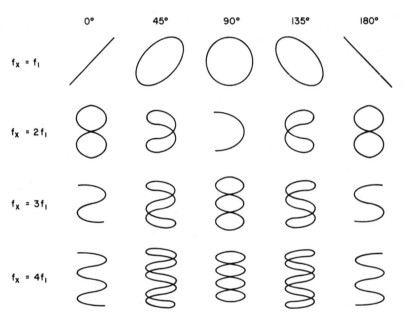

FIG. 10-4. Lissajous figures for transmitter testing.

INDEX

INDEX

PRACTICAL
OSCILLOSCOPE
HANDBOOK

Volume 2

RUFUS P. TURNER

JOHN F. RIDER PUBLISHER, INC., NEW YORK

a division of HAYDEN PUBLISHING COMPANY, INC.

Preface to Volume 2

This volume of the *PRACTICAL OSCILLOSCOPE HAND-BOOK* is devoted to applications of interest to technicians in science and industry. (Volume 1 of this set introduces the oscilloscope and explains applications primarily useful to general technicians, radio operators, servicemen, and hobbyists.) It is assumed that anyone using this volume is familiar with oscilloscope fundamentals and basic electronics.

As in Volume 1, the testing directions are as recipe-like and dross-free as possible, so that all steps may be followed efficiently. Each step-by-step procedure is a guide to a specific test or measurement and is set up for handy reference. (For a more exhaustive treatment of many of these test areas, see *Encyclopedia on Cathode-Ray Oscilloscopes and Their Uses* by J. F. Rider and S. D. Uslan and *Obtaining & Interpreting Test Scope Traces* by John F. Rider. Both books are published by John F. Rider Publisher, Inc., New York.)

Most of the tests described in this volume may be made with a relatively simple instrument. The few that require an oscilloscope with special features call attention to the fact before procedures are outlined. Also, because the technician in science or industry will often use an oscilloscope of advanced design, this volume briefly considers the extra features of the professional laboratory-type instrument in Chapter 1.

The tests that appear in this book have been chosen after careful screening of countless tests and searches. Although no book can be all things to all readers, we believe that we have chosen those tests that will be useful to the greatest number.

Altadena, California
February 1964

RUFUS P. TURNER

Table of Contents

For All Tests:
OSCILLOSCOPE SETUP PROCEDURE

Waste motion is reduced, the instrument and its operator are protected, false starts are eliminated, and reliability is increased if the operator follows a logical sequence when setting up the oscilloscope for operation. This setup procedure is the same, regardless of the test which is to be performed or the type of oscilloscope used. To avoid repetition throughout the book, this procedure is detailed below.

1. Set POWER switch to OFF.

2. If oscilloscope has plug-in units, plug desired one(s) into channel(s).

3. Turn INTENSITY, FOCUS, GAIN, and SYNC controls to zero (or to lowest settings provided).

4. Switch-off internal sweep (time base).

5. Set SWEEP selector to OFF or EXTERNAL (some instruments do not have the OFF position).

6. Set HORIZONTAL and VERTICAL POSITION controls to mid-range.

7. Plug oscilloscope into power line.

8. Throw POWER switch to ON.

9. Stand by for the full length of time recommended by the oscilloscope manufacturer as a warmup period.

10. Carefully advance INTENSITY control until spot appears on screen. To prevent burning of screen, use lowest intensity needed to see spot. If spot is not seen at any setting of INTENSITY control, it probably is deflected off screen—reset POSITION controls to bring it into view.

11. Adjust FOCUS control to sharpen spot to fine point.

12. Switch-on screen illumination and adjust to desired brightness.

13. Adjust POSITION controls to bring spot to exact center of screen.

14. Set SWEEP selector to INTERNAL RECURRENT (linear time base).

15. Switch-on internal sweep and set SWEEP FREQUENCY control to any frequency above 100 cps (or set TIMING control to any time rate under 10 msec/cm).

16. Advance HORIZONTAL GAIN control, noting that spot is deflected into a horizontal line. Verify that length of line is controllable by adjustment of HORIZONTAL GAIN control.

17. Switch-off sweep and set HORIZONTAL GAIN control to zero.

18. Advance VERTICAL GAIN control to mid-range.

19. Touch VERTICAL INPUT terminal with finger, noting that stray signal pickup by body deflects spot to give a vertical line. Verify that length of line is controllable by adjusting VERTICAL GAIN control.

20. Set VERTICAL GAIN control to zero.

21. Connect any required probe to proper input terminals.

The oscilloscope is now ready to be connected to the circuit or device under test. For safety, connect the oscilloscope *before* you switch-on the circuit power; and at the end of the test, switch-off the circuit power *before* you disconnect the oscilloscope.

Remember, this 21-step procedure is what is referred to by the direction "Set up oscilloscope" which appears in tests throughout this book.

Chapter 1

Features of Professional Oscilloscopes

The essential features of an oscilloscope, other than its cathode-ray tube and power supply, are the horizontal amplifier, vertical amplifier, and linear, recurrent sweep generator. The terminals provide horizontal amplifier input, vertical amplifier input, direct horizontal input, direct vertical input, sync input, Z-axis input, and external sweep input. The controls permit adjustment of intensity, focus, horizontal centering, vertical centering, horizontal gain, vertical gain, sweep frequency, and sync voltage amplitude. The switches permit selection of sweep type, sweep range, and sync type.

Simple oscilloscopes have all of these features, which are sometimes supplemented by a calibrating-voltage source with a control that adjusts the amplitude of this voltage. And, if the instrument is to be used for radio and television servicing, it will have a phase control and a pattern inverting switch.

Many advanced tests and measurements may be made with the simplest oscilloscope if it is properly calibrated, its operation is thoroughly understood, and its indications are correctly interpreted. Some other tests, however, either *require* that special functions be performed by the oscilloscope, or are enhanced if these functions, though not required, are available. An instrument possessing such

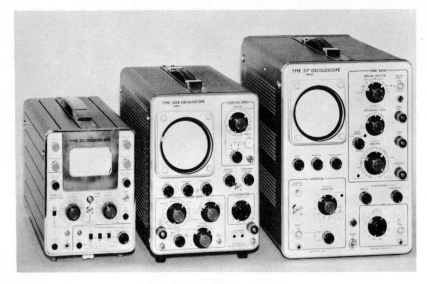

FIG. 1-1. Three professional, laboratory-type oscilloscopes. These instruments contain
many of the special features discussed
in this chapter. **Courtesy of Tektronix,
Inc.**

additional features is usually available to the industrial and engi-
neering technician. This chapter, without indulging in minute detail, describes some of the features of the advanced, laboratory-type
oscilloscope. Not every instrument will have all of these features,
but most instruments will have many of them.

1.1 WIDE-RANGE VERTICAL RESPONSE

In addition to d-c and low-frequency applications, much modern
electronic work is concerned with high frequencies and pulses. In
order to handle such signals without distorting them, the oscilloscope channels must have wider response than is commonly found
in a simple instrument. For example, the faithful reproduction of a
sharp, one microsecond pulse requires that the vertical amplifier
frequency response extend to at least 10 mc and that the vertical
transient response be excellent.

Depending upon oscilloscope type and manufacture, the vertical response of professional instruments extends from dc to frequencies as high as 1000 megacycles. Vertical amplifier rise time may be as low as 0.1 nanosecond (nsec).

1.2 HIGH VERTICAL SENSITIVITY

Increased vertical gain enables the technician to examine low-amplitude signals without using an external amplifier. This eliminates corrections for capacitance, phase shift, loading, frequency response, and transient response of such an amplifier, and minimizes instrument space.

Sensitivity (deflection factor), which depends upon oscilloscope type and manufacture, may be as acute as 2 mv/cm.

1.3 CALIBRATED TIME BASE

Most oscilloscope presentations are referenced to time as the X axis. When elapsed time or sweep rate must be known, it may be calculated from the sweep frequency. This, however, is a time-consuming chore, especially when many measurements must be made, and is susceptible to error.

A calibrated time base (sweep frequency control reading direct in time units) gives sweep time directly, thereby obviating the labor of computation. Depending upon oscilloscope type and manufacture, calibrated ranges are available between a range minimum of 1 nsec/cm to 1 μsec/cm, and a range maximum of 1 μsec/cm to 5 sec/cm.

1.4 SINGLE SWEEP

One, nonrepetitive sweep along the horizontal axis permits observation of certain "one-shot" phenomena (such as transients) and signals that are not exactly recurrent (their appearance changes during each scan of a recurrent sweep). Such a display is momentary, of course, and usually must be photographed for later study.

This kind of display is made possible by the single-sweep mechanism. A single sweep of the screen is initiated by the signal itself or by an external trigger voltage keyed manually or automatically. The screen usually is dark before and after the single-sweep presentation.

1.5 SWEEP DELAY

In the study of some signals, it is desirable that the sweep start at some selected time instant after the signal has started. The reverse also is sometimes desired. This action is afforded by sweep delay circuitry. The delay time is continuously variable, a required value chosen by adjustment of a direct-reading control.

Depending upon oscilloscope type and manufacture, calibrated sweep-delay time ranges are available between a range minimum of 0 to 2 μsec, and a range maximum of 35 nsec to 50 seconds.

1.6 PLUG-IN UNITS

For maximum versatility, some oscilloscopes are built as foundation units into which various horizontal (time-base) and vertical (amplifier) units may be plugged for desired modes of operation. These plug-ins have individual controls, selector switches, and terminals.

Some vertical plug-in units are: general-purpose single-channel amplifier, wideband single-channel amplifier; dual-trace amplifier; four-trace amplifier; differential amplifier; operational amplifier; strain gauge amplifier; and sampling amplifier.

Some horizontal (time-base) plug-in units are: conventional time-base generator; single sweep; sweep delay; and calibrated sweep delay.

A foundation oscilloscope is often acquired with only those plug-in units that are essential in the normal work of the laboratory. Other plug-ins are added when new work areas demand the extension of oscilloscope capabilities.

1.7 DUAL-BEAM TWO-TRACE OPERATION

Some oscilloscopes and plug-in units provide dual- or four-trace display by using a high-speed chopper to commutate the signals entering via the various inputs. Dual-trace operation by means of two separate guns in a single CRT is available in a few other oscilloscopes.

When such an instrument has separate identical vertical amplifier channels and separate sweep systems for the two beams, it is, in effect, two independent oscilloscopes writing on a single screen. This permits great flexibility of adjustment and increases the range of application.

1.8 IMPROVED ACCURACY AND STABILITY

Design and manufacture refinements, such as the following, increase the dependability of the laboratory oscilloscope as a quantitative measuring instrument:

Close tolerance in CRT fabrication and in deflection circuit design results in better deflection linearity and in removal of astigmatism. Flat-faced CRT's eliminate the error caused by distortion because of curvature of the conventional face. An internal graticule in the tube prevents parallax error. Close voltage regulation in the power supply stabilizes circuit operation. Scientific ventilation and circuit stabilization techniques reduce drift. Stabilization of sweep circuits eliminates pattern jitter, while adequate isolation of a-c wiring and components corrects stray modulation of the pattern. Complete shielding protects the instrument from interfering fields.

1.9 OSCILLOSCOPE ACCESSORIES

Aside from probes, auxiliary devices for oscilloscopes include *time-mark generators* (for calibrating or subdividing the horizontal axis), *pulse generators* (for sweep triggering, activation of test circuits, Z-axis blanking, synchronization, and checking of transient response), delay lines (for delaying the signal or triggered sweep by a predetermined and selectable amount), and cameras (for recording from the CRT screen).

Chapter 2

Recording from the Oscilloscope

The direct-writing oscillograph (pen-type recorder) antedated the oscilloscope by a number of years. It was natural, therefore, that some early antipathy resulted from the inability of the oscilloscope to supply a permanent record, although nobody questioned the superiority of that instrument as a high-frequency *indicator*.

Laboratorians quickly devised means of copying oscilloscope displays, and special equipment appeared. (One of the marketed devices in the 1930's was a type of reflectograph which aided the hand-copying of an oscillogram with pencil.) From the very beginning, however, photography was favored. It was not a new art, for the camera had already been used to record from nonwriting (light-beam) oscillographs.

In modern science and industry, thousands of copies are made of oscilloscope displays every year. These copies are not only useful as permanent records, but also as patterns on which some measurements may be made more conveniently than on the oscilloscope screen. Since records are needed in a great many tests and measurements, the techniques for making them are discussed in this chapter.

2.1 SELF-PROCESSING OSCILLOSCOPE CAMERA

The modern oscilloscope recorder consists of a Polaroid Land[1] camera equipped with a special lens and a mounting frame that fastens to the front of the oscilloscope and provides a hood system

---

[1] Registered trademark of Polaroid Corporation, Cambridge, Mass.

for viewing the screen. Because the Polaroid camera gives a finished picture in a few seconds without darkroom processing, records are quickly available at each step in a test.

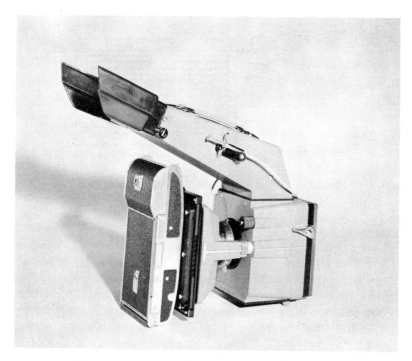

FIG. 2-1. The recording camera assembly for a modern oscilloscope. The Polaroid camera is at the lower left; the viewing hood extends upward and back above the camera. The forward chamber, which contains a mirror, is fastened to the front of the oscilloscope. Compare this figure with Fig. 2-2 and Fig. 2-3. **Courtesy of Tektronix, Inc.**

Figure 2-1 shows a camera assembly of this type.[2] The unit fastens snugly to the front of the oscilloscope (see Fig. 2-2). The familiar

[2] Type C-12, Tektronix, Inc., Beaverton, Oregon.

Polaroid camera back is at the lower left, and the viewing hood extends diagonally upward above it. The mounting adaptor is hinged so that the entire camera assembly may be swung horizontally away from the oscilloscope when direct access is desired.

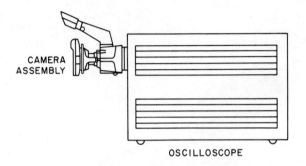

CAMERA
ASSEMBLY

OSCILLOSCOPE

FIG. 2-2. The oscilloscope camera in operating position.

Characteristics. Oscilloscope cameras are available with a number of different features. The model shown in Fig. 2-1, for example, normally is prefocused, but has an adjustment for sharp focus. The camera back may be moved horizontally or vertically, in relation to the lens, through five detented positions for recording up to five separate displays on one frame. The back may also be rotated through 90° increments. While the standard Polaroid roll-film back is shown, and is used most often (giving 3¼″ × 4¼″ prints), the assembly will also accept backs for 4″ × 5″ Polaroid sheet film, conventional cut film from 2¼″ × 3¼″ to 4″ × 5″, or a film-pack. Oscilloscope camera manufacturers provide a good selection of lens and shutter characteristics. The standard lens for the Tektronix Type C-12 camera is Wollensack Oscillo-Raptar 75 mm *f*/1.9 with 1:0.9 object/image ratio; the standard shutter is Alphax No. 3 with seven speeds from 1 sec to 1/100 sec, plus *time* and *bulb*. Several other lens-and-shutter combinations are available.

Optical Arrangement. Figure 2-3 shows the arrangement of the Type C-12 camera assembly. (The following explanation of its operation is simplified.) Rays of light from the trace and the illuminated graticule lines in the oscilloscope enter the system. In the path of

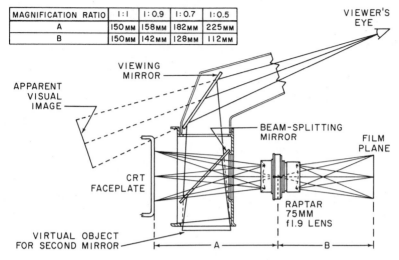

MAGNIFICATION RATIO	1:1	1:0.9	1:0.7	1:0.5
A	150MM	158MM	182MM	225MM
B	150MM	142MM	128MM	112MM

FIG. 2-3. The optical system of the Type C-12 camera. **Courtesy of Tektronix, Inc.**

these rays is the *beam-splitting mirror*. This is a transparent mirror mounted at a 45° angle. It transmits some of the rays through to the camera (represented here by lens and film plane) and reflects other rays up to the *viewing mirror*. The operator looks into the viewing mirror and sees the oscilloscope display as a virtual image. With this optical system the display can be viewed with the camera in place, even while the picture is being taken.

Film. Polaroid film types 42, 44, 47, 147, and 410 give paper prints; types 46, 46-L, and 146-L give positive transparencies. In-camera developing time is only 10 seconds for types 47 and 410. Choose film type to suit display conditions: nature of signal (whether stationary on screen, slow-moving, repetitive, or fast transient), brightness of trace, and desired speed of finishing.

The term *writing rate* in oscilloscope photography designates the highest spot speed which will produce an acceptable picture. It is expressed in centimeters per microsecond. High writing rate is needed to record fast transients, whereas a low writing rate will satisfactorily reproduce recurrent phenomena or slow sweeps. (The CRT phosphor influences the writing rate. Arranged in decreasing order starting with the highest writing rate, CRT phosphors commonly found in oscilloscope tubes are P11, P2, P1, and P7.) Film must be selected with respect to writing rate: Polaroid Type 147 (ASA rating of 10,000) has been designed for oscilloscope photography and has the highest writing rate; it is followed by Type 47 (3000 speed), very high; Type 44 (400 speed), high; and Type 42 (200 speed), low to medium.

Typical Operation. The selection of film type, exposure time, and type of display depends ultimately upon the type of phenomenon to be recorded and CRT characteristics. With a given lens aperture, the shutter speed, for example, will be fast for a bright stationary or repetitive display and slow for a dim display. When recording fast transients and other high-speed, single-shot phenomena, the shutter should be held open (bulb position) while a single sweep is triggered manually, and then closed. It is hard to generalize on these matters, since various combinations of factors, as in other kinds of photography, will give an identical picture, and because certain techniques may be recommended by the manufacturer of the oscilloscope and/or camera. Study the camera instruction manual carefully, and sacrifice a few frames of film for personal training purposes.

A dimmer, thin trace will give the best recording, but requires longer exposure. A very bright trace tends to produce halo or afterglow. The oscilloscope screen illumination must brighten the graticule lines sufficiently for sharp, clear reproduction but must not produce glare. If the display is viewed during exposure, the operator must keep his face against the hood to prevent entry of light.

The ability to make multiple exposures on a single frame is advantageous in many tests and measurements where either separate signals or the same signal at different stages must be shown close to each other for comparison. For this purpose, the camera may be slid and locked into as many as five successive vertical positions for as many separate exposures on the same frame.

General steps in making oscillogram records with a self-processing oscilloscope camera are as follows:

1. Load camera with film having proper writing rate for type of test.

2. Set up oscilloscope and make dry run of test to insure correct operation of equipment.

3. Attach camera to oscilloscope.

4. Test-operate oscilloscope while observing screen through viewing hood of camera assembly.

5. Determine exposure to be used.

6. Photograph display, following any special directions given by manufacturer of camera or oscilloscope.

7. Develop photograph in camera. (If several images are to appear on one picture, make *all* exposures before developing any.)

2.2 CONVENTIONAL CAMERA

The use of conventional film for recording from the oscilloscope has the disadvantage that darkroom processing is required. But it is used when (1) a self-processing camera is not available; (2) economy is a factor; (3) a continuous film strip is desired; or (4) processing delay is of no concern. The time between taking and viewing a picture may be reduced by accepting the developed negative in place of the paper print.

Types. Some oscilloscope camera assemblies will accept special conventional-camera backs. The Type C-12 frame described in Section 2.1, for example, will take such Graflok backs as 2¼″ × 3¼″ cut film or film pack type, 4″ × 5″ cut film type, or 120 or 620 roll film type.

In the absence of a special oscilloscope camera or adaptor, any good camera may be used if it is properly focused on the oscilloscope screen, loaded with satisfactory film, and correctly adjusted for lens opening and shutter speed.

Film. Conventional film, like Polaroid film, must be selected with due regard to writing rate. A fast film, such as one of the panchromatic types, is needed for rapid transients and other single-shot phenomena, whereas a slow film, such as one of the orthochromatic types, will serve for slow, stationary, or recurrent phenomena. With a given film, long exposure is required for a satisfactory picture of a dim, slow-speed trace; short exposure for a bright or fast trace. Aperture size and shutter speed depend upon trace brightness and type of film.

Typical Operation. There are two requisites for successful use of a conventional camera: (1) film-plane focusing (this demands a ground glass back) and (2) a hood of some kind to exclude ambient light. The latter is necessary because a camera with the usual lens must be moved farther back from the screen than an oscilloscope camera need be.

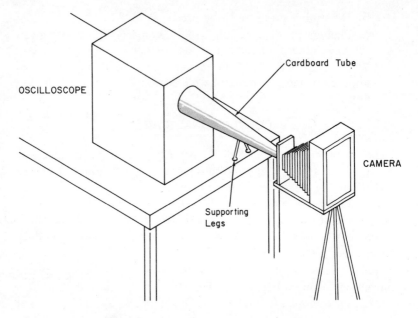

FIG. 2-4. A conventional camera setup.

A simple hood consists of a cone-shaped cardboard tube run between the camera and oscilloscope screen and fitted snugly at each end to prevent light leaks (see Fig. 2-4). The inside of the tube must be painted dull black to kill reflections. For protection against movement, the camera must be rigidly supported either with a tripod, as shown in Fig. 2-4, or by resting it on the table with the oscilloscope. The required length of the tube depends upon the focal length of the lens. To determine proper length experimentally, set up the camera in a dimly lighted room and focus it sharply on the oscilloscope trace. Then, measure the distance from screen to lens and cut the cone to that length. (A camera such as the small 35 mm models, which have no ground glass, may be opened and a piece of waxed paper stretched and taped temporarily across its open back to substitute for ground glass during focusing.) In a completely darkened room, a hood will not be needed.

The following are general steps in recording oscillograms with a conventional camera prefocused as explained above:

1. Load camera with film having proper speed for type of test.
2. Set up oscilloscope and make dry run of test to insure correct operation of equipment.
3. Set up camera with light hood (Fig. 2-4 or similar).
4. Determine exposure time and lens opening to be used, and set lens and shutter accordingly.
5. Photograph display, using exposure determined in Step 4.
6. Develop film.

2.3 INTENSIFICATION OF GRATICULE IMAGE

For good recording of the lines, the graticule lighting should be turned up high enough to make the lines shine but not so high as to produce glare. Sometimes, especially when exposure is short, this will not give sharp reproduction.

Improvement is afforded by double exposure. Expose the film first with the graticule illuminated but no trace on the screen, then expose it a second time for the trace. The graticule exposure time cannot be prescribed exactly; it should be found experimentally with each type of film used and recorded for future reference.

2.4 MOVING-FILM CAMERA

In a motion-picture camera, the film is advanced one frame at a time, each frame pausing behind the lens during exposure. In the *moving-film* camera used for special oscilloscope photography, the film is drawn by the lens continuously by an adjustable-speed motor. There is no blinking shutter. This action permits recording of a phenomenon which starts at some unpredictable instant (e.g., an occasional surge or a random pulse).

The film movement provides the horizontal sweep and, therefore, the time base. For this reason, the oscilloscope sweep must be switched off and only vertical spot deflection used. The developed film will still show the complete oscillogram referred to both axes, for the sweep is supplied mechanically by the camera. When a camera is used in which the film travels vertically with respect to the oscilloscope, the signal must be applied to the horizontal input of the oscilloscope, with the vertical input switched off. If the horizontal channel passband is too narrow for a projected test, the signal must be applied to the vertical channel (as in the first example) and either the camera or the oscilloscope laid on its side.

Film speed is continuously variable over a wide calibrated range. In one instrument of this type (General Atronics Corp. Model SM-100 Scope Recording Camera), the range extends from one-half inch per minute to 12,000 in./min. The 35 mm film or paper may also be advanced one frame at a time for single-frame recording. (This camera fits on the front of the oscilloscope and has a binocular viewer for observing the screen.)

The moving-film oscilloscope camera has been used for studying such phenomena as electrical breakdown, cosmic rays and radiation, fatigue of metals, lightning strokes, psychological and neurological responses, gas engine noise, and electrical time constants.

The moving-film camera, like the conventional still camera, uses film or sensitized paper that requires processing either in a darkroom or developing tank. This introduces a delay between the time the test is made and when the results are seen, a factor that may become inconvenient when each test in a long series is dependent on the results of the preceding one.

2.5 STORAGE OSCILLOSCOPE

The *storage oscilloscope* holds a display on the screen for an indefinite time until the operator removes it by depressing an *erase* button on the front panel. This ability to store a pattern allows short-term recording of data, as the retention time is ample enough to allow pattern dimensions to be measured on the screen. Several recorded patterns may be superimposed or spaced for comparison. The storage oscilloscope is especially useful in studies of nonrecurrent phenomena. When the storage function is switched off, the instrument can be used as a conventional oscilloscope.

The heart of this type of oscilloscope is the storage CRT. One such tube is the *memotron* (Hughes Aircraft Co., Vacuum Tube Products Division). Figure 2-5 is a simplified diagram of this tube (focus, intensity, and accelerator electrodes have been omitted for clarity). This is a 5-inch tube which may be described as having infinite and adjustable persistence. There are two electron guns: the *writing gun* is in its customary position in the rear of the tube; the *flood gun* is mounted adjacent to one pair of deflecting plates.

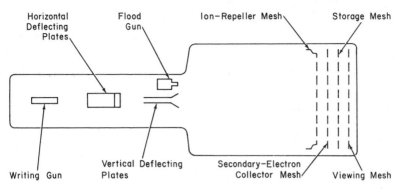

FIG. 2-5. The memotron storage tube.

Behind the face of the tube are four fine metal meshes. One of these, the *storage mesh*, is the target on which the trace is electrostatically stored. One face of this mesh is coated with a dielectric. The *viewing mesh* is next to the tube face, the *collector mesh* is behind the storage mesh, and the *ion-repeller mesh* is the rearmost. The high-velocity electron beam from the writing gun writes an electrically positive trace on the dielectric of the storage mesh; it does this by knocking electrons out of the dielectric atoms where it strikes, these secondary electrons being collected by the collector mesh. This action leaves the positive trace stored on the storage mesh after the signal has ceased. And this trace is transparent to low-velocity electrons arriving from the flood gun.

The flood gun sprays the storage target with low-velocity electrons which pass through the electrically transparent stored space on this target but not through the other areas (since the latter are at flood-gun cathode potential). Those electrons that penetrate strike the viewing screen and reproduce the trace on it. Storage results from retention by the storage mesh of the electrically transparent trace (an electrostatic charge pattern). As long as the trace remains on the target, flood-gun electrons pass through it and produce the image on the screen. The charged target in the path of these electrons thus resembles a stencil in the path of light rays.

The image may be erased by momentarily decreasing the d-c voltage of the collector mesh. This discharges the storage mesh.

Depending upon type and make, storage oscilloscopes have writing rates from 25 cm/msec to 2540 cm/msec; storage times from 1 hour to time indefinite; and erase times from 150 msec to 250 msec.

Stored traces may be photographed for permanent record, when desired.

2.6 HAND RECORDING

In the absence of recording equipment, a hand tracing may be made from an oscilloscope screen. This requires more care than skill and is limited to stationary patterns or those of long duration.

Transparent Overlay.   A disc of transparent plastic is best for hand recording, as it gives a clear view of the trace. It must be thick enough to prevent parallax but not so thin that it puckers or wrinkles —0.01 inch seems satisfactory. A graticule may be inscribed on one face and the tracing done on the opposite one.

To make a record:

1. Place the disc over the face of the oscilloscope.

2. Carefully align the graticule of the disc with that of the oscilloscope.

3. Either attach the disc to the face with two or three small dots of two-sided adhesive tape or hold it firmly in place.

4. Use a well-sharpened grease pencil to trace the pattern. This pencil gives a solid, readable line which later is easily removed by rubbing with tissue. It also does not scratch the plastic.

Translucent Overlay.   A thin paper disc may be used in lieu of the transparent plastic but it requires a brighter trace. The disc may be cut from draftsman's tracing paper, and a graticule ruled on one side. If drawing is inconvenient, discs may be cut from thin graph paper, such as K. & E. No. 359T-5G (10×10 div./inch).

The recording procedure is the same as that for the transparent disc, except that a medium pencil (grade HB lead) should be used. However, when using the paper disc, care must be taken that the trace brightness is not high enough to burn the screen.

Discharging Electrified Disc.   A plastic or paper disc may become charged with static electricity when it is lifted from its storage place, especially if it is drawn across a dry, polished surface. When it is placed against the CRT face, its charge may distort the trace. To prevent this, discharge the disc before attaching it to the oscilloscope by touching it momentarily to a cold water pipe or by breathing on it.

Chapter 3

Checking Physical Quantities

The oscilloscope plays an important role in the study of diverse physical quantities. Here, the oscilloscope is valuable because it can show not only the magnitude of a quantity but also how that quantity varies with respect to another variable such as time. Its versatility is due to its accommodation of any quantity, non-electrical as well as electrical, that can be converted into a proportional voltage. Thus, an instrument designed originally for the study and measurement of electrical quantities is found in such comparatively remote fields as acoustics, astronautics, aviation, crime detection, hydraulics, mathematics, medicine, meteorology, music, navigation, ordnance, and psychology. The list could be expanded almost endlessly.

Practical applications are described in this chapter. For detailed treatment of the many other applications in each category, the reader is referred to the practical literature of his field of interest: industrial electronics, computers, acoustics and sound, etc.

3.1 CURRENT BY PROBE METHOD

Measurement of current by the shunt-resistor method is described in Chapter 5 of Volume 1. That method requires that the circuit be broken for insertion of the resistor and restored after the measurement is completed. While the inserted resistance is kept as low as possible, its presence nevertheless alters circuit performance to some degree. To avoid this source of possible error, the test may be made with a more expensive *current probe* which requires no physical connection to the circuit under test and does not appreciably load the circuit.

Figure 3-1 is a simplified diagram of the current probe. This device resembles the familiar clamp-type ammeter used in power-frequency electrical measurements and operates in a somewhat similar manner, but the clamp transformer element is much smaller. For simplicity, the probe handle is not shown here, only the pickup element, which is mounted on its end.

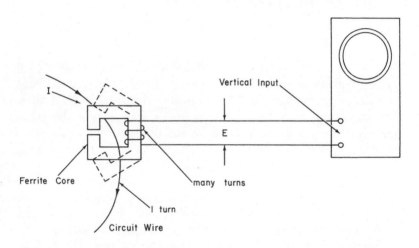

FIG. 3-1. Use of the current probe.

The pickup element consists of a tiny square-O-shaped ferrite core around which a coil of wire is wound. The core is swiveled so that it may be temporarily opened up, as shown by the dotted lines, when the probe handle is squeezed. This allows the core to be closed around a circuit wire carrying the current of interest. This forms a transformer with the wire acting as a one-turn primary against the probe coil which forms a many-turn secondary. The current, I, induces a voltage, E, across the secondary proportional to the step-up turns ratio, and this voltage is applied to the vertical amplifier input of a voltage-calibrated oscilloscope.

The current is read in terms of the deflection voltage, indicated by the oscilloscope, and the current factor of the probe (given by the probe manufacturer and usually expressed in mv/ma).

The Hewlett-Packard AC-21F Current Probe has an output of 1 mv per milliampere. The same company's 456A probe provides ranges of 1 ma to 1 amp. Because the core of the current probe is ferrite rather than iron, wide frequency response is obtained (the passband of the 456A probe, for example, is 60 cps to 4 mc).

Test Procedure

1. Set up voltage-calibrated oscilloscope.

2. Connect current probe to VERTICAL INPUT terminals.

3. Set VERTICAL GAIN control for standard deflection voltage if this is given by the probe manufacturer.

4. Switch-on test circuit.

5. Clamp probe pickup around current-carrying circuit wire.

6. Read voltage, E, from oscilloscope screen.

7. Calculate current from voltage, E, and probe current factor.

Note: If vertical gain is set for reference deflection, current may be read direct from screen. Thus, for a 1 mv/ma probe, gain may be set for a deflection of 1 mv per screen division. The screen then will indicate 1 ma/division, and no calculation is needed.

3.2 TIME

The time interval of a phenomenon often must be determined. This applies not only to electrical quantities, but also to non-electrical physical phenomena which can be converted into voltage. High-speed phenomena cannot be timed with a stop watch and only infrequently can they be timed with an electromechanical recorder.

For this purpose, the horizontal axis of the oscilloscope may be time-calibrated. The internal sweep of some oscilloscopes is calibrated to read direct in time rate, e. g., microseconds per centimeter (see Section 1.3), and the time interval may be determined from distance measurements made along the horizontal axis.

With a single-trace oscilloscope, time may be determined (1) in terms of time-calibrated sweep; (2) in terms of sweep frequency; or (3) from a timing pattern substituted for the signal pattern by fitting it into the same horizontal interval. With a dual-trace oscilloscope, a timing wave may be displayed along with the pattern under study, as a sort of "time yardstick." Each of these methods is discussed below.

Use of time-calibrated sweep:

1. Display one, stationary cycle of the phenomenon on screen, using oscilloscope internal sweep and internal sync.[1]

2. Read time factor from direct-reading SWEEP RANGE controls.

3. Measure distances along horizontal axis between zero (start of signal) and points of interest on display.

4. Convert these distances to time units by multiplying each by the sweep time factor.

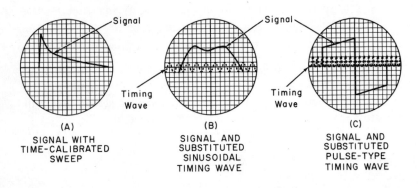

(A)	(B)	(C)
SIGNAL WITH	SIGNAL AND	SIGNAL AND
TIME-CALIBRATED	SUBSTITUTED	SUBSTITUTED
SWEEP	SINUSOIDAL	PULSE-TYPE
	TIMING WAVE	TIMING WAVE

FIG. 3-2. Timing with a single-trace oscilloscope.

Example: Figure 3-2A shows one "cycle" of a transient which builds up suddenly and then slowly decays to zero. It is desired to know time t_1, at which the transient reaches its peak, time t_2, at which it has decayed to 50 percent of peak amplitude, and time t_3, at which it reaches zero. Assume that the oscilloscope sweep reading

---

[1] The word *cycle* is used here generically. Actually, the phenomenon might not be a cycle in the sense of a complete a-c alternation, but a unilateral pulsation, response curve, or similar display.

for the stationary pattern is 100 μsec/cm and that each screen division in Fig. 3-2A is 1 centimeter. Then t_1 = 0.5 cm = 50 μsec, t_2 = 2.5 cm = 250 μsec, and t_3 = 15 cm = 1500 μsec = 1.5 msec.

Use of frequency-calibrated sweep:

When the oscilloscope sweep is direct-reading in frequency (f) rather than in time units, time intervals may be determined in terms of f:

1. As in the preceding illustration, display one stationary cycle of the phenomenon on screen, as in Fig. 3-2A, using internal sweep and internal sync.

2. Read frequency (f) from direct-reading sweep range controls.

3. Calculate the period of this phenomenon: $T = 1000/f$, where T is in milliseconds and f is in cps.

4. Measure horizontal distance D (in screen divisions) between start and end of pattern, and calculate time factor: X (in milliseconds per screen division) $= T/D$.

5. Measure horizontal distance (in screen divisions) between zero (start of signal) and each point of interest on pattern.

6. Convert these distances into time by multiplying each by time factor X obtained in Step 4.

Example: For the transient pulse in Fig. 3-2A, it is desired to know time t_1, at which the pulse reaches its peak amplitude, time t_2, at which it has decayed to 50 percent of peak amplitude, and time t_3, at which it reaches zero. Assume that the oscilloscope sweep frequency for the stationary pattern is 1000 cps. Then T = 1 msec and X = 0.0666 msec/div = 66.6 μsec/div. The time intervals may then be calculated: t_1 = 0.5 div = 33.3 μsec, t_2 = 2.5 div = 166.6 μsec, and t_3 = 1000 μsec = 1 msec (15 div).

If the oscilloscope sweep controls are not direct reading in frequency, the frequency may be determined in the following manner after the sweep and sync controls have been set for one stationary cycle of the phenomenon:

1. Without disturbing setting of sweep and sync controls or of HORIZONTAL GAIN control, connect a calibrated variable-frequency oscillator or signal generator to VERTICAL INPUT terminals in place of device or circuit under test.

2. Vary oscillator frequency and output amplitude until one stationary cycle appears on screen.

3. Read frequency from oscillator dial. This is the sweep frequency (f).

Substitution of Timing Wave. Time intervals along the horizontal axis may be measured with a timing wave. This is a signal of known frequency or timing factor. Either a sine wave or special pulse-type timing wave may be used. The procedure is to substitute the timing wave for the display, measure the horizontal distance between points of interest by counting the timing-wave cycles or pulses between these points, and calculate time interval in terms of pulse rate or sine-wave period.

Example—Sine Wave. It is desired to know the duration of the pulse shown in the solid line in Fig. 3-2B. This pulse is seen to start at the 3rd screen division and end at the 17th. Follow this procedure:

1. Adjust oscilloscope sweep and internal sync for a single, stationary cycle of the phenomenon.

2. Note horizontal screen divisions coinciding with beginning and end of pattern (in this case, the 3rd and 17th).

3. Without disturbing setting of sweep, sync, or gain controls, connect variable-frequency signal generator to VERTICAL INPUT terminals in place of device or circuit under test.

4. Adjust frequency and output amplitude of generator to give as many *stationary* cycles as can be accurately counted on screen. (See dotted-line pattern in Fig. 3-2B.)

5. Read generator frequency f in cps.

6. Calculate period: T (in milliseconds) $= 1000/f$. This is the time interval indicated by the distance between adjacent sine-wave peaks.

7. Adjust HORIZONTAL POSITION control to align a positive peak of timing wave with point at which test signal started (3rd screen division here).

8. Count number (n) of positive peaks from starting point of signal to point at which signal ended (17th screen division here).

9. Calculate pulse duration: $t = T(n - 1)$.

For illustration, assume that the generator is tuned to 1000 cps. The distance between adjacent peaks of the sinusoidal timing wave then represents T = 1 msec. Exactly eight positive peaks are counted from the start of the signal pulse to the point at which it ends. The pulse duration then (from Step 9) is t = 1(8 −1) = 7 msec.

Example—Timing Wave. A pulse-type timing wave gives a series of sharp spikes which may be aligned with screen lines and counted more accurately than the sine-wave cycles of the preceding example. This wave is obtained from a pulse generator or *time-mark generator* and is often called a *comb* from its shape. Figure 3-2C shows the appearance of a pulse-type timing wave (dotted line) used to measure the period of a tilted square wave (solid line) for which it is substituted.

The procedure is the same as with the sine-wave timing signal, except that the spike tips are counted for n. The time-mark generator reads direct in spike interval, e. g., the Hewlett-Packard 1783A Time-Mark Generator delivers spikes at 0.1, 1, and 10-μsec intervals. If this generator were used for the presentation given in Fig. 3-2C, and set for 10-μsec spacing, the period of the square wave would be indicated as 140 μsec.

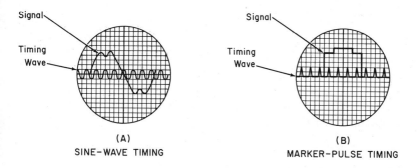

(A)   (B)
SINE-WAVE TIMING   MARKER-PULSE TIMING

FIG. 3-3. Timing with a dual-trace oscilloscope
(superimposed patterns).

Direct Comparison. With a dual-trace oscilloscope, either a sine-wave or pulse-type timing signal may be displayed simultaneously with the phenomenon under study and the two can be easily compared. The test signal is applied to one pair of VERTICAL INPUT terminals and the timing signal to the other pair. The PATTERN POSITION controls may be adjusted to superimpose the timing signal on the test signal (Fig. 3-3A and B) or separate them by any desired distance (Fig. 3-4A and B). This method has the advantage that the test signal and the timing signal are both on the screen at all times, so that the timing signal may be used directly as a "time yardstick" laid alongside of or on top of the test signal.

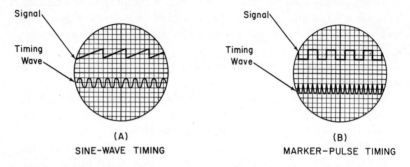

(A)   (B)
SINE-WAVE TIMING   MARKER–PULSE TIMING

FIG. 3-4. Timing with a dual-trace oscilloscope (separated patterns).

3.3 PULSE DELAY

Figure 3-5A shows one setup for checking the time interval between an input pulse and output pulse introduced by a delay device. The latter may be a delay line, monostable multivibrator, digital circuit, or similar device. An oscilloscope having three vertical inputs is required.

Test Procedure

1. Set up oscilloscope.

2. Switch-on internal sweep.

3. Set SYNC SELECTOR switch to INTERNAL.

4. Set up equipment as shown in Fig. 3-5A. Switch-on pulse generator, time-mark generator, and delay device (if it is powered).

5. Set pulse generator for desired pulse duration and repetition rate.

6. Set SWEEP FREQUENCY and SYNC controls for a single, stationary input pulse and output pulse, as shown in Fig. 3-5B.

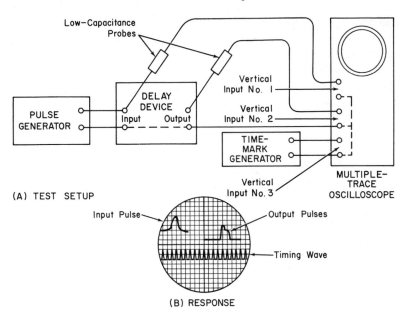

FIG. 3-5. Pulse delay measurement.

7. Set HORIZONTAL and VERTICAL GAIN controls and pulse generator output for desired pulse pattern width and height.

8. Determine delay interval by counting timing spikes between input pulse and output pulse and referring to time-mark generator calibration (see Section 3-2).

9. Determine pulse duration by counting timing spikes under pulse and referring to time-mark generator calibration.

3.4 PULSE CHARACTERISTICS

Amplitude, shape, and time characteristics of a pulse may be determined by means of voltage and time measurements on the oscilloscope screen. Because of their steep sides and short duration, pulses will be reproduced faithfully only by a high-speed oscilloscope, i.e., one in which wide frequency response and excellent transient characteristics are provided. Pulses come in many sizes and shapes but all have certain features in common, such as duration, rise time, fall time, and peak amplitude. Some may show overshoot, ringing, or tilt.

Figure 3-6A shows one type of distorted pulse with its various characteristics identified. Amplitudes, such as preshoot voltage E_1, overshoot voltage E_3, and pulse peak voltage E_4, are measured from

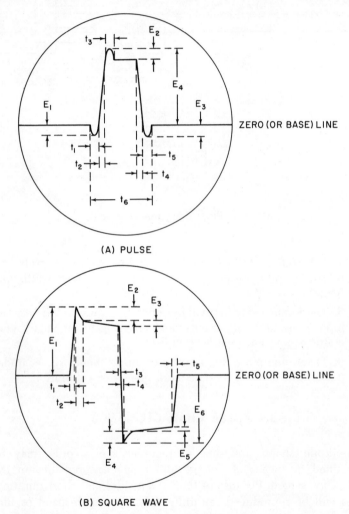

(A) PULSE

(B) SQUARE WAVE

FIG. 3-6. The principal characteristics of steep signals.

the zero (or base) line on the voltage-calibrated screen; overshoot voltage E_2 is measured from the flat top of the pulse to the top of the pip. Time intervals are measured along the time-calibrated horizontal axis: t_1 is the duration of the preshoot; t_2 is the pulse rise time; t_3 is the duration of the leading overshoot; t_4 is the pulse fall time; t_5 is the duration of the trailing overshoot; and t_6 is the pulse duration. The pulse repetition rate (pulses per second) is equal to the sweep frequency that will display one pulse on the screen.

3.5 SQUARE WAVE CHARACTERISTICS

Like pulses (Section 3.4), square waves have amplitude, time, and shape characteristics that can be checked only with a high-speed oscilloscope.

Figure 3-6B shows one type of distorted square wave with various important characteristics identified. Amplitudes such as positive peak voltage E_1 and negative peak voltage E_6 are measured from the zero (or base) line on the voltage-calibrated screen; positive overshoot voltage E_2 is measured from the top of the pip to the start of the slope; positive tilt E_3 is measured from the top to the bottom of the slope; negative overshoot voltage E_4 is measured from the start of the slope of the negative half-cycle to the top of the pip; and negative tilt E_5 is measured from the top to the bottom of the slope of the negative half-cycle. Time intervals are measured along the time-calibrated horizontal axis: t_1 is the positive half-cycle rise time; t_2 is the duration of the positive overshoot; t_3 is the positive half-cycle fall time; t_4 is the negative half-cycle rise time; and t_5 is the negative half-cycle fall time.

3.6 TRANSIENTS

Electrical transients result from such causes as induction, switching (mechanical and electronic), accidental breakdown (as in insulation), controlled breakdown (as in a gas or semiconductor), and operation of certain RC circuits. Because transients, like pulses, are rapid phenomena often characterized by steep rise and fall, their accurate display requires a high-speed oscilloscope. When a transient is nonrecurrent, the oscilloscope must have single sweep (triggered by the transient), and either photography or storage must be employed to record the pattern for study and measurement.

Non-electrical transients include those surges arising in systems operated by, or responding to, pressure, vibration, impact, sound, and light. By means of suitable transducers, these transients may be converted to voltages for presentation to the oscilloscope.

The way in which an oscilloscope is used to display an electrical transient depends upon whether the latter is primarily a current or a voltage. For a voltage, the vertical input must be connected to the transient-voltage source; usually this means connecting across a component or branch of a circuit. For a current, a noninductive resistor (across which the transient current develops a proportional voltage drop) must be inserted in the circuit and the vertical input connected across this resistor. This shunt resistance must be very low (0.1 to 10 ohms), with respect to the circuit resistance, to minimize its effect upon performance. In some instances, a current probe may be used in place of the resistor to avoid circuit interruption.

Whenever the transient amplitude is high enough, direct input to the vertical deflecting plates should be used. This avoids possible deformation by the vertical amplifier channel. In most tests, a low-capacitance probe will be desirable to minimize the effect of the oscilloscope input circuit on the transient circuit.

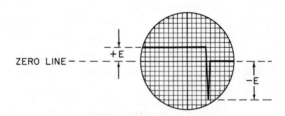

FIG. 3-7. The turn-off switching transient.

There are many kinds of transients. In Fig. 3-6, for instance, the preshoot and overshoots are transients. Figure 3-7 shows the type of transient which often appears when inductive circuits are switched off. (Such a circuit contains a transformer winding, relay, or choke coil.) The circuit has been switched on and a steady d-c voltage

(+E) appears across the inductive component. When the circuit is switched off, this voltage does not immediately fall to zero but, because of counter emf, it falls momentarily to a high negative value (−E) and then rises back to zero. A transient spike of this kind can, under some conditions, be high enough in voltage to damage equipment.

From Fig. 3-7, it is obvious that both voltage and time of the transient may be measured from the pattern on the screen.

3.7 ELECTRICAL NOISE

Electrical noise is generated in the majority of circuits where it arises as an unwanted by-product. The sound it produces in headphones or loudspeaker is mostly sustained and, depending upon its nature and origin, varies from harsh grating (sometimes with intermixed popping) to hissing or rushing.

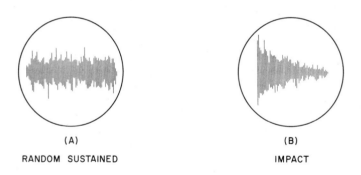

(A)   (B)

RANDOM SUSTAINED   IMPACT

FIG. 3-8. Electrical noise patterns.

A noise voltage is a mixture of an enormous number of frequencies and waveforms having some statistical relation to each other. The picture it produces on the oscilloscope screen, therefore, is diffuse, showing occasional sharp transients. Figure 3-8A shows the typical pattern produced by sustained random noise. Figure 3-8B shows the damped transient pattern produced by impact noise, such as might result from a single electrical burst. Peak amplitude generally is of chief interest in noise-voltage tests, and (to obtain a ratio of merit) this is compared with signal voltage in the same circuit. But sometimes the component frequencies must be examined.

The way in which an oscilloscope is used to display electrical noise depends upon whether a voltage or current must be sampled. For a voltage, the vertical input must be connected to the noise-voltage source; usually this means connecting across a component or branch of a circuit. For a current, a noninductive, low-noise resistor (across which the noise current develops a proportional voltage) must be inserted in the circuit and the vertical input connected across this resistor. This shunt resistance must be very low (0.1 to 10 ohms), with respect to the circuit resistance, to minimize its effect upon circuit performance. In some instances, such as transient testing, a current probe may be used in place of the resistor to avoid circuit interruption.

Test Procedure

1. Set up voltage-calibrated and time-calibrated oscilloscope.

2. Switch-on internal sweep.

3. Set SYNC SELECTOR switch to INTERNAL.

4. Connect VERTICAL INPUT terminals to voltage or current point in test circuit, as explained above.

5. Set SWEEP FREQUENCY control for noise display similar to Fig. 3-8A.

6. Set HORIZONTAL and VERTICAL GAIN controls for desired width and height of pattern.

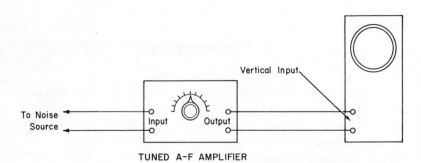

TUNED A-F AMPLIFIER

FIG. 3-9. The setup for noise frequency components.

7. Read peak-to-peak amplitude of noise from voltage-calibrated screen.

8. Read time intervals on noise pattern (horizontal axis), if required.

9. Photograph pattern for permanent record.

When it is desired to investigate the frequency components of noise, use the setup shown in Fig. 3-9. A sharply tunable a-f amplifier is connected ahead of the oscilloscope.[1] This amplifier is tuned successively to each frequency of interest and amplitude and time characteristics are checked. Because most frequencies are present only randomly in the noise mixture, a photograph of the display is needed in order to hold the display long enough for study and measurement.

3.8 ACOUSTIC NOISE AND SOUND

The measurement of acoustic noise and sound is similar to that of electrical noise, explained in Section 3.7, except that the sound or noise in this instance is picked up with a microphone. The latter thus serves as a sound-to-voltage transducer. A high-quality sound-calibrated capacitor microphone is used with a preamplifier which boosts the microphone output voltage to a level suitable for the oscilloscope input.

Figure 3-10A shows the test setup used when only the noise/sound amplitude (and, perhaps, time characteristics) are of interest. The display will resemble Fig. 3-8. Figure 3-10B shows insertion of a tunable amplifier to separate any desired frequency component in the spectrum of the noise signal for study and evaluation.

Through use of the sound-calibration data supplied by the manufacturer of the microphone and preamplifier, the voltage-calibrated screen of the oscilloscope may be calibrated in decibels, and sound intensity levels read directly without calculations.

---

[1] Such continuously tunable instruments operating in the 20–20,000-cps range include tuned amplifiers, sound and vibration analyzers, and wave analyzers.

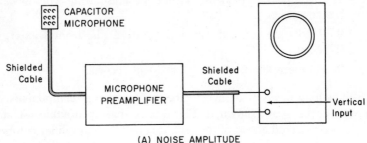

(A) NOISE AMPLITUDE

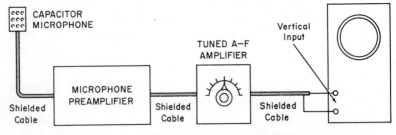

(B) NOISE AMPLITUDE AND FREQUENCY

FIG. 3-10. The setup for acoustic noise and sound.

3.9 VIBRATION

The measurement of vibration is similar to the measurement of electrical noise (Section 3.7) and acoustic noise and sound (Section 3.8), except that the vibration is sampled with a *vibration pickup* attached to the vibrating body. This transducer usually is a piezo-electric device which delivers an a-c voltage proportional to the acceleration of the vibrating body. It is supplied with a suitable preamplifier. One commercial vibration pickup system (General Radio Type 1560-P11) includes self-contained integrator networks which provide output voltages proportional to velocity and displacement. For vibration studies, the vibration pickup and preamplifier are substituted for the microphone and preamplifier in Fig. 3-10A and B.

If only vibration and time characteristics (intensity, acceleration, displacement, velocity, time) are of interest, use the setup in Fig.

3-10A. When it is desired to separate single vibration frequencies for study and measurement, use the setup in Fig. 3-10B. Often, a given frequency occurs only randomly, and the display must be photographed in order to hold it long enough for measurement. Through use of vibration-calibration data supplied by the manufacturer of the pickup and preamplifier, the voltage-calibrated screen of the oscilloscope may be calibrated for direct reading of intensity, acceleration, velocity, or displacement.

3.10 ROTATIONAL SPEED

Various transducers are available for converting the rotational speed of a machine to a proportional voltage or frequency. They operate on either magnetic, capacitive, or photoelectric principles. A common form of tachometer-type magnetic transducer is a miniature generator which is operated by the rotating wheel or shaft under observation. Either an a-c or d-c generator might be used, but ac generally is chosen because of the ease with which it may be amplified.

Depending upon make and model, the generator is supplied to deliver either (1) an output voltage proportional to speed, or (2) a frequency proportional to speed. The output of the first type is specified by the manufacturer in rpm/volt, and the output of the second in rpm/cps. Capacitive and photoelectric transducers are of the frequency type, and require no mechanical attachment to the rotating device. For the voltage type, use the test setup in Fig. 3-11A; for the frequency type, use Fig. 3-11B.

Test Procedure (Voltage-Type Transducer)

1. Set up voltage-calibrated oscilloscope.

2. Set oscilloscope VERTICAL SELECTOR switch for ac or dc conforming to the pickup output.

3. Connect pickup to VERTICAL INPUT terminals, as shown in Fig. 3-11A.

4. Couple pickup mechanically to rotating device.

5. Read voltage from calibrated screen of oscilloscope.

6. Calculate revolutions per minute: multiply indicated voltage by rpm/v figure supplied by pickup manufacturer.

Note: Either of the voltage-measuring methods (with or without sweep) may be used. (See Chapter 5, Volume 1.)

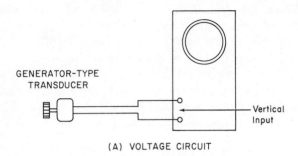

(A) VOLTAGE CIRCUIT

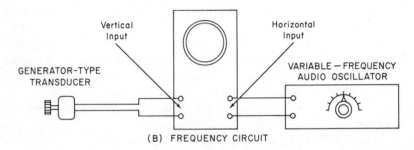

(B) FREQUENCY CIRCUIT

FIG. 3-11. The setup for rotational speed.

Test Procedure (Frequency-Type Transducer)

1. Set up oscilloscope.

2. Switch-off internal sweep.

3. Set SYNC SELECTOR switch to EXTERNAL.

4. As shown in Fig. 3-11B, connect pickup to VERTICAL INPUT terminals and an accurate variable-frequency audio oscillator to HORIZONTAL INPUT terminals.

5. Couple pickup (if a generator) mechanically to rotating device.

6. Adjust HORIZONTAL and VERTICAL GAIN controls for pattern of desired size.

7. By tuning oscillator, identify pickup frequency by means of Lissajous figures (see Section 6.1, Volume 1).

8. Calculate revolutions per minute: multiply indicated frequency by rpm/cps figure supplied by pickup manufacturer.

Note: Either of the common frequency-measuring methods may be used. (See Chapter 6, Volume 1.)

3.11 OBJECT SPEED

The speed (velocity) of a rapidly moving object, such as a bullet, missile, projectile, or vehicle, may be measured with the setup shown in Fig. 3-12A. This scheme reveals the instant at which the moving object passes each of two points separated by an accurately known distance. From the time interval and distance, the speed may be calculated.

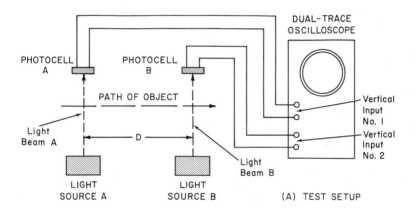

(A) TEST SETUP

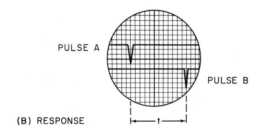

(B) RESPONSE

FIG. 3-12. Object speed.

In Figure 3-12A, light sources A and B project their beams to light-sensitive pickups A and B, respectively. (The latter may be either self-generating photocells or d-c powered phototubes.) The photo-devices are connected to the vertical inputs of a dual-trace oscilloscope. Distance D between the two light beams is known with precision. As the opaque object travels in the direction indicated, it interrupts the first light beam, causing the output of photocell A to drop momentarily to zero and produce a pulse (A) on the screen (see Fig. 3-12B). The object then interrupts the second light beam, causing the output of photocell B to drop momentarily to zero and produce a second pulse (B) on the screen. This effect is so rapid that the display must either be photographed or obtained with a storage oscilloscope. The distance between the pulse peaks may be measured along the time-calibrated horizontal axis, and the object speed determined from the indicated time interval and distance D.

Test Procedure

1. Set up time-calibrated dual-trace oscilloscope. Instrument must be either a storage oscilloscope or equipped with a camera.

2. Switch-on internal recurrent sweep.

3. Set SYNC SELECTOR switch to EXTERNAL.

4. Set up equipment as shown in Fig. 3-12A and measure D in feet.

5. Set sweep to trial rate.

6. Set HORIZONTAL and VERTICAL GAIN controls to trial positions.

7. Set TRACE POSITION controls to space traces as shown in Fig. 3-12B.

8. If camera is used, hold shutter open in bulb position.

9. Propel object and close shutter after exposure (if storage oscilloscope is used, simply propel object, the two pulses will remain on screen until erased).

10. Develop picture.

11. If second pulse is off screen, increase sweep frequency (decrease sweep time rate) and repeat Steps 8, 9, and 10.

12. Along time-calibrated horizontal axis, measure distance between pulse peaks and convert this to seconds (t) from sweep time calibration.

13. Calculate object speed: V (in ft/sec) = D/t.

If a multi-trace oscilloscope is used, a timing wave (see Section 3.2) may be fed into a third vertical input, and the pulse-to-pulse time determined from the timing-wave pattern which appears simultaneously with the pulses.

3.12 STRAIN

Abundant means are available for measuring stress and strain of a static nature. But the dynamic type—strain that varies rapidly with time—is conveniently measured from oscilloscope photographs or from the display retained by a storage oscilloscope.

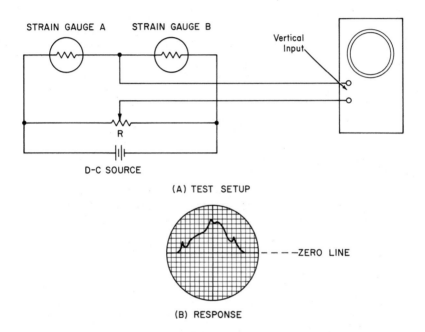

(A) TEST SETUP

(B) RESPONSE

FIG. 3-13. Strain measurement.

Figure 3-13A shows a setup for checking dynamic strain with a conventional high-speed oscilloscope. Here, two resistance wire-type strain gauges (A and B) and a potentiometer (R) are connected in a d-c bridge circuit. One strain gauge is cemented to the structure under test and the other is an identical unit used as the reference arm of the bridge. Initially, when the structure is not stressed, potentiometer R is adjusted to balance the bridge. At this time, the bridge output voltage is zero and the oscilloscope is not deflected. When the structure is subsequently stressed, the resistance of the attached strain gauge is altered, the bridge consequently is unbalanced, and the proportional d-c output voltage deflects the oscilloscope. The result is a plot of strain vs. time, such as is shown in Fig. 3-13B.

When using the oscilloscope camera, hold the shutter open (bulb position), stress the structure, close the shutter, and develop the picture. If the strain pulse bleeds off the screen, decrease the sweep frequency (increase sweep time rate). The pattern reveals voltage amplitude (vertical axis) and time intervals (horizontal axis). The voltage may be converted to strain units (e. g., micro-inches/inch) by reference to the calibration figure (micro-inches/inch/volt) supplied by the strain gauge manufacturer.

3.13 PRESSURE

Photographs from a conventional oscilloscope or displays retained by a storage oscilloscope are invaluable in the study and measurement of dynamic pressure—pressure that changes with time (often in the sharp manner of a transient). Such pressures are encountered in engine cylinders, gun barrels, pumps, hydraulic and pneumatic piping, and similar places. Various types of pressure-to-voltage transducers are available, including strain gauge, piezoelectric, and capacitive models.

The strain gauge type consists basically of a resistance-type strain gauge cemented to a pressure-actuated diaphragm. This pickup may be operated as one arm of a resistance bridge, as in Fig. 3-13A. The pickup is installed in the wall of a chamber in which the pressure will be generated. With no pressure present, potentiometer R is adjusted to balance the bridge; the bridge output voltage at this point is zero, and the oscilloscope is not deflected. Later, pressure distends the diaphragm, stretching the attached strain gauge and changing its resistance. This unbalances the bridge, and a proportional voltage is delivered to the oscilloscope. The resulting plot of pressure vs. time resembles the strain display shown in Fig. 3-13B.

As in the preceding example, when using the oscilloscope camera, hold the shutter open (bulb position), operate the test system, close the shutter, and develop the picture. If the pressure pulse bleeds off screen, decrease the sweep frequency (increase sweep time rate).

The pattern reveals voltage amplitude (vertical axis) and time intervals (horizontal axis). The voltage may be converted to pressure units (e.g., lbs/sq. in.) by reference to the calibration figure (psi/v) supplied by the pressure pickup manufacturer.

The piezoelectric pressure pickup is also widely used. This type has the advantage that it is self-generating, and therefore needs no battery or other power supply. Neither does it require the bridge circuit shown in Fig. 3-13A but may be connected directly to a high-gain oscilloscope or through a preamplifier to a low-gain oscilloscope.

3.14 ACCELERATION

For the study of fluctuations in acceleration as a function of time, a resistance-type accelerometer may be connected in an oscilloscope bridge circuit, as shown in Fig. 3-13A. The accelerometer replaces one of the strain gauges in this circuit and a fixed resistor replaces the other.

The bridge is balanced, by adjustment of potentiometer R, either at zero acceleration or some preselected value of acceleration. The bridge output at this point is zero and the oscilloscope is not deflected. When the acceleration subsequently changes, the bridge unbalances and a proportional voltage is applied to the oscilloscope. The result is a display of acceleration vs time, similar to the strain pattern shown in Fig. 3-13B.

As in both preceding examples, when using the oscilloscope camera hold the shutter open (bulb position), operate the test system, close the shutter, and develop the picture. If the acceleration pattern bleeds off screen, decrease the sweep frequency (increase sweep time rate). The pattern reveals voltage amplitude (vertical deflection) and time intervals (horizontal deflection). The voltage may be converted to acceleration units (ft/sec^2) by reference to the calibration figure (ft/sec^2 per volt) supplied by the accelerometer manufacturer.

3.15 BASIC MEASUREMENT OF CAPACITANCE

Capacitance may be measured from a capacitor discharge curve. This requires a d-c oscilloscope with triggered single sweep that is of the storage type or equipped with a camera.

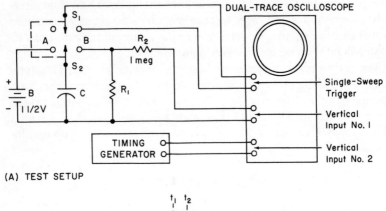

(A) TEST SETUP

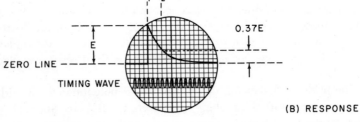

(B) RESPONSE

FIG. 3-14. Basic measurement of capacitance.

Figure 3-14A shows the test setup. C is the capacitor under test, and B is a 1½-volt battery for charging the capacitor. R_1 is a precision 1-watt noninductive resistor. (The resistance of R_1 should be 100K for testing capacitances between 10 pf and 0.1 μfd, 10K for 0.1–10 μfd, 1K for 10–100 μfd, and 100 ohms for 100–1000 μfd.) R_2 is a 1-megohm ½ watt resistor to isolate R_1 from the oscilloscope input resistance. When the DPDT test switch (S_1-S_2) is thrown to position A, capacitor C is charged by battery B; when this switch is thrown to position B, the capacitor discharges through resistor R_1. At this time, section S_1 of the switch triggers a single sweep of the oscilloscope.

The shape of the discharge curve which is displayed on the screen is shown in Fig. 3-14B. When S_1-S_2 is thrown to position B, the voltage across R_1 rises suddenly to the fully charged value E at time t_1. Immediately, the capacitor begins to discharge through R_1. At time t_2, the voltage has fallen to 37 percent of the fully charged value.

The unknown capacitance (in μfd) is determined from the time interval between t_1 and t_2 (in msec) and the resistance of R_1 (in ohms): $C = 1000(t_2\text{-}t_1)/R$.

If a dual-trace oscilloscope is used, a convenient timing wave (the lower pattern in Fig. 3-14B) may be displayed simultaneously with the discharge curve by means of a timing generator connected to the second vertical input. If a single-trace oscilloscope is used, the time interval $t_2\text{-}t_1$ may be measured (1) from the calibrated sweep (Section 3.2); (2) from the calibrated horizontal axis (Section 3.2); or (3) by means of a timing wave recorded below the display by a second exposure after the main display has been photographed or stored. (The timing signal is applied to the VERTICAL INPUT terminals in place of the capacitor test circuit, and the VERTICAL POSITION control is adjusted to place the timing wave below the main display.)

Test Procedure

1. Set up storage or camera-equipped oscilloscope. This instrument must have provision for externally (switch) triggered single sweep and must have d-c input.

2. Set up equipment as shown in Fig. 3-14A.

3. Set SWEEP FREQUENCY (TIME RATE) controls for trial rate.

4. Set HORIZONTAL and VERTICAL GAIN controls to trial position.

5. Set SYNC SELECTOR switch to EXTERNAL.

6. Hold camera shutter open (bulb position).

7. Hold switch $S_1\text{-}S_2$ at position A for about 2 seconds.

8. Throw switch to position B.

9. After exposure, close shutter and develop picture.

10. If discharge curve bleeds off screen before it falls to the 0.37 E point, decrease sweep frequency (increase sweep time rate) and repeat Steps 6 to 9.

11. On oscillogram, locate time point t_2 at which voltage amplitude is 0.37 maximum (it is not necessary that vertical axis be voltage-calibrated).

12. Measure time interval $(t_2\text{-}t_1)$ between maximum voltage point (E) and 0.37 E voltage point.

13. Calculate capacitance: $C = 1000(t_2-t_1)/R$, where C is in μfd, t_1 and t_2 in msec, and R in ohms.

14. If useful portion of discharge curve cannot be confined to screen, select another value for R_1, as explained above.

If the oscilloscope has low vertical sensitivity, the voltage of battery B may be increased to produce a pattern of suitable height. However, voltage E must not exceed the maximum safe d-c operating voltage of the capacitor under test.

3.16 BASIC MEASUREMENT OF INDUCTANCE

Inductance may be measured by means of a time-constant method similar to that described for capacitance in the preceding section. A d-c oscilloscope with triggered sweep is required, and this instrument must be either camera-equipped or of the storage type.

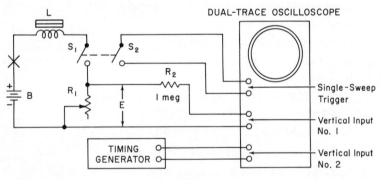

(A) TEST SETUP

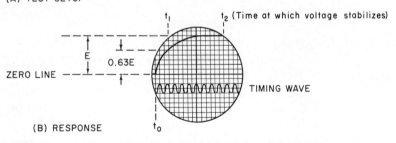

(B) RESPONSE

FIG. 3-15. Basic measurement of inductance.

Figure 3-15A shows the test setup. L is the inductor under test and B is a battery or well-filtered d-c power supply for forcing a current through it. R_1 is a rheostat for adjusting the current level. This unit must be calibrated and fitted with a direct-reading OHMS dial, or its resistance when it is set during the inductance test must be measured with the rheostat temporarily removed from the circuit. With a given battery voltage, R_1 must be set (with the switch closed and a d-c ammeter or milliammeter temporarily inserted at point X) for maximum safe operating current of the inductor. The resistance of the rheostat at this setting must be noted. Since the internal resistance of an inductor varies with make and model, the battery voltage must be selected to suit the circumstances and cannot be specified here.

Resistor R_2 is a 1-megohm ½ watt unit used to isolate R_1 from the oscilloscope input resistance. When the DPST test switch (S_1-S_2) is open, no current flows through the inductor, and the oscilloscope receives no signal voltage. When the switch is closed, section S_1 closes the d-c circuit, and current flows through L and R_1 in series. This produces a voltage drop across R_1, which is the signal voltage applied to the oscilloscope. At the same time, section S_2 closes the trigger circuit and initiates a single sweep of the oscilloscope. Because of the counter emf generated by the inductor, the current (and voltage E) cannot reach its maximum value instantaneously, but increases exponentially, as shown by the curve (Fig. 3-15B) which is displayed on the screen. At time t_1, the voltage has risen to 63 percent of its final (maximum, steady) amplitude E. The unknown inductance (in henrys) is determined from the time interval between t_0 and t_1 (t_0 = zero) and resistance R_1.

If a dual-trace oscilloscope is used, as in Fig. 3-15A, a convenient timing wave (the lower pattern in Fig. 3-15B) may be displayed simultaneously with the response curve by means of a timing generator connected to the second vertical input. If a single-trace oscilloscope is used, the time interval t_1-t_0 may be measured (1) from the calibrated sweep (see Section 3.2); (2) from the time-calibrated horizontal axis (Section 3.2); or (3) by means of a timing wave recorded below the display by a second exposure after the initial display has been photographed or stored. (The timing signal is applied to the VERTICAL INPUT terminals in place of the inductor test circuit, and the VERTICAL POSITION control is adjusted to place the wave below the main display.)

Test Procedure

1. Set up d-c storage or camera-equipped oscilloscope. This instrument must have provision for externally (switch) triggered single sweep.

2. Measure d-c resistance of inductor and record as R_c.

3. Set up equipment as shown in Fig. 3-15A.

4. Insert a d-c ammeter or milliammeter temporarily at point X, close switch S_1-S_2, adjust rheostat R_1 for maximum rated inductor current, and record rheostat resistance setting as R_p. Then, open S_1-S_2, remove meter, and restore circuit.

5. Set SWEEP FREQUENCY (TIME RATE) to trial rate.

6. Set HORIZONTAL and VERTICAL GAIN controls to trial position.

7. Set SYNC SELECTOR switch to EXTERNAL.

8. Hold camera shutter open (bulb position).

9. Close switch S_1-S_2.

10. After exposure, close shutter, open switch, and develop picture.

11. If response curve bleeds off screen before it reaches maximum amplitude E, decrease sweep frequency (increase sweep time rate) and repeat Steps 8 to 10.

12. On oscillogram, locate time point t_1 at which voltage amplitude is 0.63 E (it is not necessary that vertical axis be voltage-calibrated).

13. Measure time interval (t) between zero (t_0) and t_1.

14. Calculate inductance: $L = 0.001\ t(R_c + R_p)$, where L is in henrys, t is in milliseconds, and R_c and R_p are in ohms.

Chapter 4

Checking Components

In test circuits for checking component parts, an oscilloscope is connected and driven in a manner similar to that of a wideband v-t voltmeter. But whereas the vtvm indicates only the amplitude of a test signal, the oscilloscope can display a plot of amplitude against a second variable, such as time, and will show waveform, presence of transients, and other supplementary phenomena as well. The information it presents instantly could otherwise be acquired only by making a series of many tests and then plotting the data point by point. The oscilloscope is especially useful, therefore, in those component tests entailing response curves, transient phenomena, phase relations, and combinations of variables.

The tests given in this chapter are the kind in which the oscilloscope has particular value. There are many more tests in which the oscilloscope functions only as a vtvm, jobs which (except in equipment shortages) might be left to the less expensive meter. It is difficult, of course, to draw a sharp line between component testing and the checking of physical quantities, but the distinction made should be evident in most examples. However, some overlap is unavoidable (see, for example, Sections 3.3, 3.7, 3.15, and 3.16).

4.1 MAGNETIC COMPONENTS

Many magnetic-core devices are used in electronics. These include transformers, choke coils and similar inductors, magnetic amplifiers, saturable reactors, and computer memory cores. Hysteresis and saturation are important properties of the core materials and may be determined by oscilloscope methods in a fraction of the time required for data taking and curve plotting.

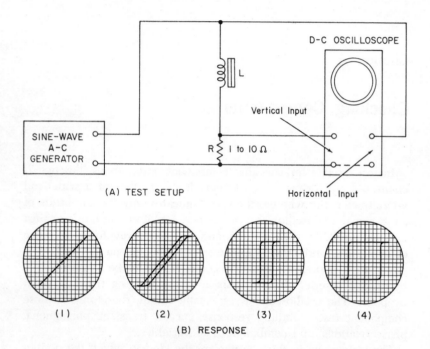

FIG. 4-1. Magnetic saturation and hysteresis.

Figure 4-1A shows a setup for these tests. Here, L is an inductor under test. (A temporary coil may be wound around a sample core.) A low, noninductive resistance (1 to 10 ohms) is connected in series with the inductor. The sine-wave a-c generator has adjustable output and forces a current through L and R. This generator must be tunable to the desired test frequency and its power output must be sufficient for saturation of the inductor. The oscilloscope must have identical d-c horizontal and vertical channels to eliminate phase difference. The entire generator output voltage is applied to the horizontal input as a sinusoidal sweep voltage. The voltage drop across resistor R is applied to the vertical input as a current signal. If the inductor has neither hysteresis nor saturation at any generator voltage, the response is a 45°, right-tilted straight line, as in Fig. 4-1B1. If either of these properties is present, however, the shape of the pattern will lie between the extremes represented by Fig. 4-1B2 and 4-1B4. Vertical deflection is proportional to flux density B (+ gausses above the zero line and − gausses below); horizontal deflection is proportional to magnetizing force H (+ oersteds to the right of the vertical center line and − oersteds to the left).

Test Procedure

1. Set up d-c oscilloscope having voltage-calibrated horizontal axis.

2. Switch-off internal recurrent sweep.

3. Set SYNC SELECTOR switch to EXTERNAL.

4. Position spot at exact center of screen.

5. Connect equipment as shown in Fig. 4-1A. If only a sample of core material is available, wind a coil of insulated wire on it, using as many turns as possible.

6. Set HORIZONTAL and VERTICAL GAIN controls to mid-range or to calibration point.

7. Increase generator output, noting that pattern enlarges on screen. Continue to increase output until bending of upper and lower ends of pattern shows saturation is reached. Double-line trace (Figs. 4-1B2, 4-1B3, 4-1B4) indicates hysteresis.

8. If hysteresis loop pattern bleeds off screen, readjust HORIZONTAL and VERTICAL GAIN controls.

9. Compare hysteresis loop with specifications by manufacturer of core material or device under test.

10. From voltage-calibrated horizontal axis, note peak voltage (+ and −) at which saturation occurs.

11. Repeat test at as many frequencies as required.

Magnetic material for computer cores, magnetic amplifiers, and bistable devices is expected to show hysteresis. A square loop (Fig.

4-1B4) is prized. In material for transformer cores and other power devices, however, hysteresis is an important source of loss and is undesirable. (The energy lost per cycle per cubic centimeter of material is $W = \frac{1}{4} \pi \int H \, dB$, where $\int H \, dB$ is the area of the hysteresis loop. This area may be measured approximately by totaling the areas of the screen squares within the loop, or closely by running a planimeter around the photographed loop.)

4.2 FERROELECTRIC COMPONENTS

Certain crystalline materials, such as barium titanate, triglycene sulfate, and GASH (guanadine aluminum sulfate hexahydrate), exhibit electrostatic hysteresis. The latter may be regarded as the electrostatic equivalent of the magnetic effect described in Section 4.1. Two-plate capacitors with single-crystal ferroelectric material as the dielectric have been used in dielectric amplifiers (electrostatic equivalent of the magnetic amplifier), bistable devices, and computer memories.

Figure 4-2A shows a setup for testing saturation and hysteresis of ferroelectrics. Here, X is the test unit. A ferroelectric capacitor may simply be connected in this position; but if only the ferroelectric material is available for the test, a thin, flat slab of it must be provided with metal plates (as shown in Fig. 4-2A) to form a test capacitor. The ferroelectric unit is connected in series with a fixed capacitor, C (0.1 to 0.5 μfd). The sine-wave a-c generator has adjustable output and forces a current into the capacitive circuit (X and C in series). This generator must be tunable to the desired test frequency and its maximum output voltage must be sufficient to saturate the ferroelectric. The oscilloscope must have identical d-c horizontal and vertical channels to eliminate phase difference.

The entire generator output voltage is applied to the horizontal input as a sinusoidal sweep voltage. The voltage across capacitor C is applied to the vertical input as a current signal. If sample X has neither saturation nor hysteresis at any generator voltage, the response pattern is a 45°, right-tilted straight line, as in Fig. 4-2B1. If either of these properties is present, however, the shape of the pattern will lie between the extremes represented by Fig. 4-2B2 and 4-2B4. Vertical deflection is proportional to electric charge Q (+ coulombs above the zero line, and — coulombs below); horizontal

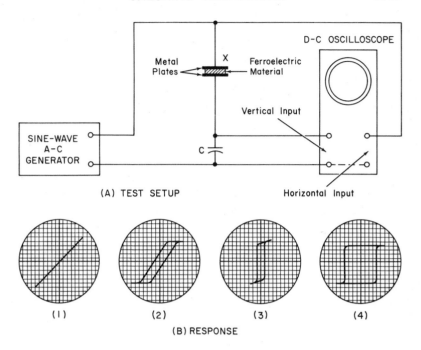

(A) TEST SETUP

(B) RESPONSE

FIG. 4-2. Electrostatic saturation and hysteresis.

deflection is proportional to applied voltage V (+ volts to the right of the vertical center line, and − volts to the left).

Test Procedure

1. Set up d-c oscilloscope having voltage-calibrated horizontal axis.

2. Switch-off internal recurrent sweep.

3. Set SYNC SELECTOR switch to EXTERNAL.

4. Position spot at exact center of screen.

5. Connect equipment as shown in Fig. 4-2A. Connect a ferroelectric capacitor as shown at X; if only a sample of material is available, make a capacitor by providing it with metal plates.

6. Set HORIZONTAL and VERTICAL GAIN controls to mid-range.

7. Increase generator output, noting that pattern enlarges on screen. Continue to increase output until bending of upper and lower ends of pattern shows saturation is reached. Double-line trace (Figs. 4-2B2, 4-2B3, 4-2B4) indicates hysteresis.

8. If hysteresis loop bleeds off screen, readjust HORIZONTAL and VERTICAL GAIN controls.

9. From voltage-calibrated horizontal axis, note peak voltage (+ and −) at which saturation occurs.

10. Compare hysteresis loop with specifications by producer of ferroelectric material.

11. Repeat test at as many frequencies as required.

Ferroelectric material for computer memory cells, dielectric amplifiers, voltage-tuned circuits, and bistable devices is expected to show hysteresis. A square loop (Fig. 4-2B4) is prized. In dielectric material for conventional capacitors, however, hysteresis is a source of loss and is undesirable. (The energy lost per cycle per cubic centimeter of the material is $W = \frac{1}{4} \pi \int V \, dQ$, where $\int V \, dQ$ is the area of the hysteresis loop. This area may be measured approximately by totaling the areas of the screen squares within the loop, or closely by running a planimeter around the photographed loop.)

4.3 RELAYS

Relays may be checked for make, break, make-time, and break-time. A d-c oscilloscope with an externally (switch) triggered single sweep is required. If a dual-trace instrument is available, a timing generator may be connected to the second vertical input, as shown in Fig. 4-3A and B; if a single-trace oscilloscope is used, its horizontal axis must be time-calibrated.

A relay which makes and breaks cleanly will give a rectangular wave pattern (Fig. 4-3C1); bouncing contacts will produce amplitude fluctuations, generally at closure (Fig. 4-3C2). Make-time t_1 (Fig. 4-3C3) is the interval between application of voltage and actual closure of the relay; break-time t_2 is the interval between interruption of voltage and opening of the relay.

Figure 4-3A shows a test setup for a d-c relay (RY). For a given battery (B) voltage, resistance R is chosen to limit the contact current to the value specified by the relay manufacturer. When switch S is closed, the relay closes and the voltage across resistor R is applied as a signal to the vertical input. Closure of S also initiates a single sweep in the oscilloscope.

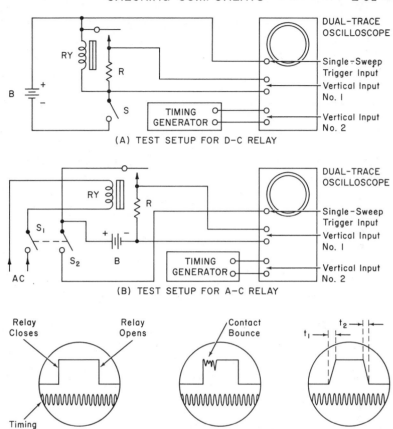

FIG. 4-3. Relay tests.

Test Procedure

1. Set up d-c oscilloscope having triggered single sweep. Instrument must be either camera-equipped or storage type. If oscilloscope is dual-trace, connect timing generator to second vertical input; if single-trace, time-calibrate horizontal axis.

2. Switch-off internal recurrent sweep.

3. Set SYNC SELECTOR switch to EXTERNAL.

4. Connect equipment as shown in Fig. 4-3A.

5. Set HORIZONTAL and VERTICAL GAIN controls to trial position.

6. If camera is used, hold shutter open (bulb position), next close and open switch S, then close shutter, and, finally, develop picture. (If oscilloscope is storage-type, only close and open switch S.)

7. Inspect oscillogram for contact bounce (Fig. 4-3C2): measure amplitude of bounce components on voltage-calibrated vertical axis; measure time duration of bounce components on time-calibrated horizontal axis or with aid of timing wave.

8. Measure make-time and break-time (t_1 and t_2, respectively, in Fig. 4-3C3) on time-calibrated horizontal axis or with aid of timing wave.

9. If pattern bleeds horizontally off-screen, increase sweep time; if its height is unsatisfactory, readjust VERTICAL GAIN control.

Figure 4-3B shows a test setup for an a-c relay (RY). In this arrangement, ac is supplied to the relay coil, but dc from battery B is supplied to the oscilloscope as signal and trigger voltage. The contacts of DPST switch S_1-S_2 must close or open at the same instant. When this switch is closed, section S_1 makes the a-c circuit and the relay closes. At the same time, section S_2 closes the battery circuit, causing dc to flow through the relay contacts and resistor R (which produces the vertical signal), thereby initiating the sweep. As in the d-c circuit, resistance R is chosen, for a given battery (B) voltage, to limit the contact current to the d-c value specified by the relay manufacturer.

The test procedure is the same as that explained for the d-c relay. A defective a-c relay may exhibit chattering contacts, a trouble revealed by a ripple on the flat-top of the rectangular wave pattern.

4.4 VIBRATORS

Figure 4-4 shows test setups for power supply vibrators: the nonsynchronous type in Fig. 4-4A and the synchronous (self-rectifying) type in Fig. 4-4B. In each circuit, C_1 and RFC form an r-f hash filter, and C_2 is a high-voltage buffer capacitor. Figure 4-5 shows sample test patterns.

To test either type of vibrator under actual operating conditions, resistance-load the power supply to its rated output, and connect the oscilloscope vertical input across the primary winding of the power transformer, T.

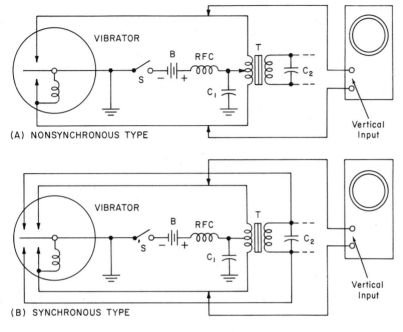

FIG. 4-4. Vibrator tests.

Test Procedure

1. Set up voltage-calibrated and time-calibrated oscilloscope.

2. Switch-on internal sweep.

3. Set SYNC SELECTOR switch to INTERNAL.

4. Set HORIZONTAL and VERTICAL GAIN controls to mid-range or to calibration point.

5. Connect equipment as shown in Fig. 4-4 (A or B, whichever applies).

6. Close switch S.

7. Adjust SWEEP FREQUENCY and SYNC controls for two stationary cycles on screen (see Fig. 4-5, B to E).

8. Readjust HORIZONTAL and VERTICAL GAIN controls, if necessary, for suitable width and height of pattern.

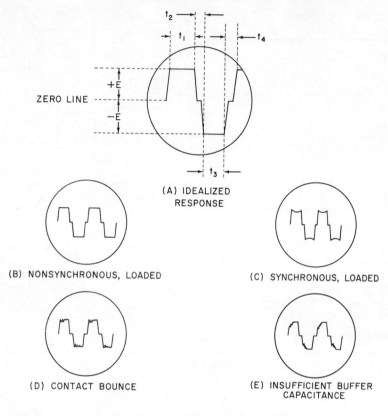

(A) IDEALIZED RESPONSE

(B) NONSYNCHRONOUS, LOADED

(C) SYNCHRONOUS, LOADED

(D) CONTACT BOUNCE

(E) INSUFFICIENT BUFFER CAPACITANCE

FIG. 4-5. Vibrator test patterns.

Figure 4-5A is an idealized version of the vibrator square-wave voltage developed across the transformer primary. Positive peak voltage ($+E$) and negative peak voltage ($-E$) are measured from the zero line on the voltage-calibrated vertical axis; time intervals t_1, t_2, t_3, and t_4 are measured along the time-calibrated horizontal axis. (If a dual-trace oscilloscope is used, a timing wave may be displayed simultaneously with the pattern.) Intervals t_1 and t_3 show the length of time the vibrator contacts are closed on positive and negative half-cycles, respectively. Interval t_2 shows the length of time taken to open "on the positive side" and close "on the negative side"; interval t_4 shows the similar switching time from negative back to positive. For efficient operation and long vibrator life, t_1 and

t_3 must be long with respect to t_2 and t_4. (A desirable relationship is $t_1 = t_3 = 9(t_2 + t_4)$. This means that the ON time, $t_1 + t_3$, is 90 percent of the square-wave cycle.)

Numerous facts regarding vibrator operating conditions may be deduced from the observed waveform. Figures 4-5B and C show typical waveforms for nonsynchronous and synchronous units, respectively. In Fig. 4-5C, the peak curvature is due to full-load voltage drop in the transformer primary and does not indicate trouble. Figure 4-5D shows the effect of contact bounce. Too low a buffer (C_2) capacitance gives the effect shown in Fig. 4-5E. In it, there are fluctuations similar to those resulting from contact bounce, but the leading corners of the square-wave half-cycles are noticeably rounded as well.

4.5 CHOPPERS

Choppers (modulators) are used to convert d-c signals to ac for subsequent amplification in many instrumentation and control circuits. Electromechanical and electronic (semiconductor-type) choppers are available. In all of these devices, an a-c driving (or *excitation*) voltage converts the d-c input to a square-wave output voltage, the amplitude of which is proportional to the d-c voltage. The electromechanical chopper is a highly refined vibrator which is externally excited; the transistor-type chopper is an electronic switch which accomplishes the same purpose.

Figure 4-6A shows a test setup for the electromechanical chopper. The d-c is applied to the D-C INPUT terminals. The a-c driving voltage (supplied by an oscillator, multivibrator, or power line) is applied to the A-C EXCITATION terminals. The reed, set into vibration by the exciting magnetic field, alternately closes the d-c circuit through the top and bottom halves of the transformer primary, generating a square-wave voltage across this winding. As in vibrator testing (Section 4.4), the primary voltage is presented to the vertical input of a voltage-calibrated, time-calibrated oscilloscope.

Figure 4-6B shows a semiconductor-type chopper employing two transistors, Q_1 and Q_2. The d-c signal is applied to the D-C INPUT terminals. The square-wave a-c excitation voltage, applied through

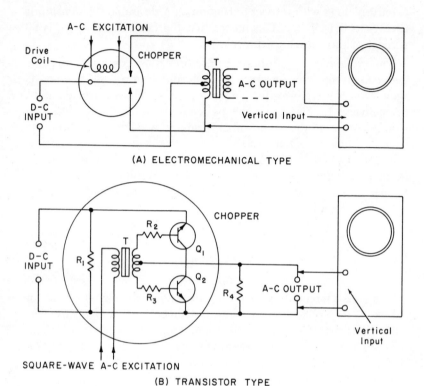

(A) ELECTROMECHANICAL TYPE

(B) TRANSISTOR TYPE

FIG. 4-6. Chopper tests.

isolating transformer T, switches the transistors into alternate conduction, resulting in a square-wave output voltage with amplitude proportional to the d-c input. The a-c output voltage is presented to the vertical input of a voltage-calibrated, time-calibrated, a-c oscilloscope.

Test Procedure

1. Set up voltage-calibrated, time-calibrated oscilloscope.

2. Switch-on internal sweep.

3. Set SYNC SELECTOR switch to INTERNAL.

4. Set HORIZONTAL and VERTICAL GAIN controls to mid-range or to calibration point.

5. Connect equipment as shown in Fig. 4-6 (A or B, which-ever applies).

6. Apply a-c excitation and maximum rated d-c input to chopper.

7. Adjust SWEEP FREQUENCY and SYNC controls for two stationary cycles on screen.

8. Readjust HORIZONTAL and VERTICAL GAIN controls for suitable width and height of pattern.

9. Measure amplitude of square wave on voltage-calibrated vertical axis; examine time characteristics on time-calibrated horizontal axis. (If dual-trace oscilloscope is used, a timing wave may be displayed simultaneously with the square-wave pattern.)

10. Inspect square wave for amplitude and time characteristics similar to those given for the vibrator in Figs. 4-5A and D. Also examine square wave for switching transients (overshoots on turn-on and/or turn-off).

11. With d-c signal disconnected but with a-c excitation applied, check output for electrical noise (see Section 3.7)—Test electromechanical chopper first with D-C INPUT terminals opened, and then with D-C INPUT terminals short-circuited; test transistor chopper with D-C INPUT terminals open.

4.6 MICROPHONES

Figure 4-7 shows a test setup for microphone performance. Whether or not a preamplifier is required depends upon oscilloscope vertical gain and microphone output voltage. A high-level microphone may be connected directly to the vertical input, as in Fig. 4-7A; a carbon microphone will require a battery (B), current-adjusting rheostat (R), and step-up transformer (T), as shown in the insert in Fig. 4-7. The output of a low-level microphone must be built up with a suitable preamplifier having high gain and low distortion, as in Fig. 4-7B.

Test residual noise level by shielding the microphone from sounds, using full gain of the oscilloscope and preamplifier, and following the procedure outlined in Section 3.7. For other tests, excite the microphone with acoustic energy delivered by a calibrated, low-distortion sound source. Use internal sweep and sync of the oscilloscope to reproduce several cycles of the sound frequency. Vary the

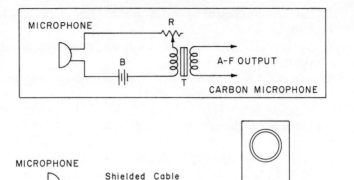

CARBON MICROPHONE

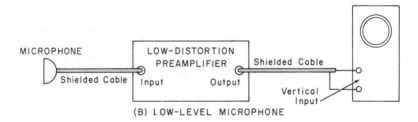

(A) HIGH-LEVEL MICROPHONE

(B) LOW-LEVEL MICROPHONE

FIG. 4-7. Microphone tests.

sound frequency to check microphone response throughout its specified range and examine the microphone output for distortion and amplitude variation.

See also *Acoustic Noise and Sound* in Section 3.8.

4.7 POTENTIOMETER NOISE

Electrical noise generated by a current-carrying potentiometer may be checked with the setup shown in Fig. 4-8A. Battery B supplies the maximum rated d-c voltage of potentiometer R.

With the oscilloscope internal sweep switched-on, a clean, straight, horizontal-line trace (Fig. 4-8B1) is obtained at any setting of potentiometer R, whether the potentiometer wiper arm is resting or in motion. If there is "static" noise in the potentiometer, a jagged noise pattern similar to Fig. 4-8B2 is obtained with the arm resting on the noisy spot. If there is "dynamic" noise in the potentiometer, the noise pattern is generated only when the arm is moved on the resistance element. For continuous cycling in dynamic tests, the arm often is moved back and forth by a suitable motor. Measure the noise-voltage amplitude on the calibrated vertical axis of the oscilloscope. Photograph the display for a permanent record.

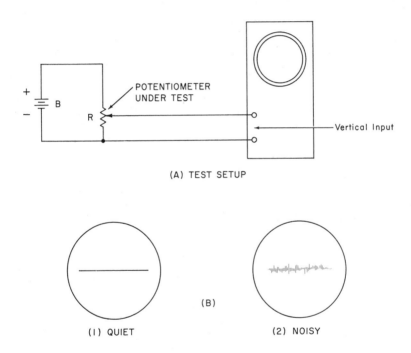

FIG. 4-8. Potentiometer noise test.

Any sweep frequency above 100 cps usually is satisfactory for this test. The SYNC SELECTOR switch should be set to EXTERNAL. It should be noted that voltage-divider action in the potentiometer varies when the position of the wiper arm is changed. This results in a vertical-input signal of varying mean d-c level. It is because of this action that the a-c oscilloscope is recommended.

4.8 SEMICONDUCTOR RECTIFIER, VISUAL TEST

The current-voltage characteristic curve of a semiconductor rectifier is presented instantly by the d-c oscilloscope in the test setup
shown in Fig. 4-9. For this purpose, both the horizontal and vertical
axis of the oscilloscope must be d-c voltage-calibrated, with the zero
point at center screen. When this is done (see Fig. 4-10A), a positive horizontal-input voltage will deflect the spot from center screen
(zero point) to the right, and a negative horizontal-input voltage
will deflect it to the left. Similarly, a positive vertical-input voltage
will deflect the spot from center screen upward, and a negative vertical-input voltage will deflect it downward. The oscilloscope must
have identical horizontal and vertical channels to eliminate phase
difference.

The rectifier (D) under test is connected in series with a 1-ohm
resistor (R) and the secondary winding of transformer T. The secondary voltage must be the maximum recommended operating voltage of the rectifier, and may be closely adjusted with the Variac.
The a-c voltage alternately biases the rectifier anode positive and
negative, causing first forward current and then reverse current to
flow through resistor R. The resulting voltage drop across the resistor
is applied to the vertical input and deflects the spot rapidly up and
down. At the same time, the a-c voltage is applied to the horizontal
input and deflects the spot rapidly from side to side. The vertical
deflection is proportional to the rectifier current flowing through R,
and the horizontal deflection is proportional to the applied voltage.
The instantaneous position of the spot is governed, therefore, by the
voltage and its polarity and by the current and its polarity at that
instant. This causes the response curve to be traced and instantly
produced, as far as the eye is concerned, as in Fig. 4-10B. When R
is 1 ohm, current may be read directly on the voltage-calibrated vertical axis (e. g., 0.1 v deflection = 0.1 amp = 100 ma). This is the
same curve obtained by successively applying d-c voltages to the
rectifier and checking corresponding d-c currents. Figure 4-10C and
D shows curves indicating faulty operation.

Test Procedure

1. Set up oscilloscope dc-calibrated as explained above.

2. Switch-off internal sweep.

3. Set SYNC SELECTOR switch to EXTERNAL.

4. Set HORIZONTAL and VERTICAL GAIN controls to calibrated point.

5. Connect equipment as shown in Fig. 4-9.

6. Adjust Variac for transformer secondary voltage corresponding to maximum rated applied voltage of rectifier D.

7. Observe curve on screen and compare with those in Fig. 4-10.

8. Check voltage and current at any points of interest on curve.

9. Photograph curve for permanent record or later study.

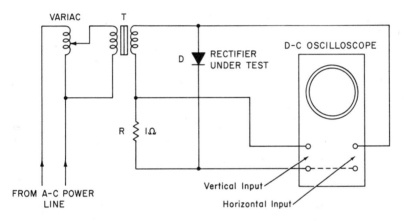

FIG. 4-9. Semiconductor rectifier test.

4.9 SEMICONDUCTOR DIODE, VISUAL TEST

The current-voltage characteristic curve of a small-signal semiconductor diode may be obtained with the kind of test setup described for the rectifier in Section 4.8. A problem, however, is the large ratio of normal forward to reverse voltage for the diode; a forward voltage of the same amplitude as the reverse voltage at which a diode is rated will damage the diode, and the rectifier test circuit (Fig. 4-9) delivers the same forward and reverse voltages. The diode can be checked in this type of circuit, but the voltage swing must be limited to the maximum forward value. This is not high enough for a realistic test in the reverse direction.

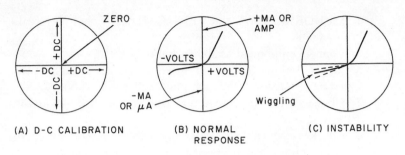

(A) D-C CALIBRATION   (B) NORMAL RESPONSE   (C) INSTABILITY

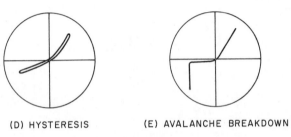

(D) HYSTERESIS   (E) AVALANCHE BREAKDOWN

FIG. 4-10. Rectifier response patterns.

What is needed is a lopsided a-c test voltage which swings a short distance in the forward direction (positive half-cycle) and a long distance in the reverse direction (negative half-cycle). Such a voltage may be obtained with the arrangement shown in Fig. 4-11A. Here, separate high-vacuum rectifier tubes (V_1, V_2), chosen for linear conduction near zero, alternately switch a low positive (forward) voltage and high negative (reverse) voltage to the anode of the diode (D) under test. Tube V_1 conducts when the upper secondary terminal is positive, and R_1 is adjusted for maximum rated forward voltage across the diode. When the upper secondary terminal swings negative, V_1 cuts off and removes R_1 from the circuit, but V_2 now conducts, delivering a negative half-cycle of voltage to diode D at the full peak voltage of the secondary minus the small drop in the tube. Figure 4-11B shows the positive and negative voltage sequence applied to the diode. It is only necessary to adjust the Variac for maximum rated reverse voltage across diode D, and then to adjust R_1 for maximum rated forward voltage across D.

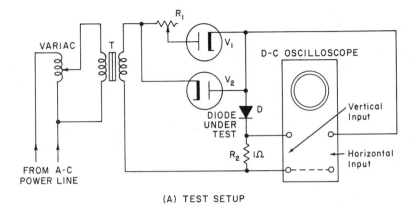

(A) TEST SETUP

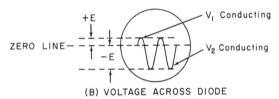

(B) VOLTAGE ACROSS DIODE

FIG. 4-11. Semiconductor diode test.

The test procedure is the same as for the semiconductor rectifier (see Section 4.8). The oscilloscope must have identical horizontal and vertical channels to eliminate phase difference.

4.10 DIODE SWITCHING CHARACTERISTICS

Diodes used in digital computers must switch and recover rapidly. Switching characteristics are readily determined from oscillograms. For this purpose, a high-speed oscilloscope is required (i.e., one having wide frequency response and excellent transient characteristics). The horizontal axis of the instrument must be time-calibrated.

Figure 4-12A shows one test setup (various others are specified by diode manufacturers, consumers, and military agencies). The diode (D_1) initially is forward-biased by the current (I_f in Fig. 4-12B) from the 250 v d-c supply, adjusted by means of rheostat R_1 and milliammeter M. A negative square wave, developed across

50-ohm resistor R_2, switches the diode voltage rapidly to a high negative value. But because carriers, stored during the forward conduction, linger at the diode junction, the diode does not cut off immediately. Instead, a high reverse current (I_p in Fig. 4-12B) flows momentarily as a steep transient. As the carriers are then swept out of the junction, the reverse current falls to its low steady-state value, I_r. The diode thus alters the square wave to the shape shown in Fig. 4-12B. Forward and reverse currents flow through resistor R_4, and the voltage drop across this resistor actuates cathode follower V_2, which applies the distorted square wave to the oscilloscope vertical input. Tube diode V_1 clamps the R_4 voltage to a safe level for the oscilloscope.

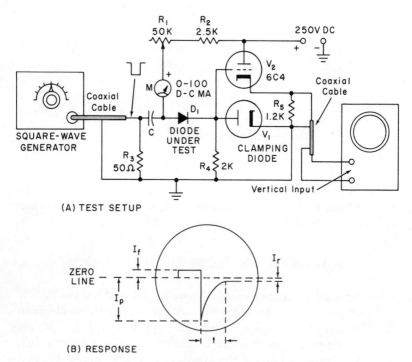

FIG. 4-12. Diode recovery time.

The interval t between the negative peak and the point at which the reverse current has reached its low steady-state value is the diode *recovery time*.

Test Procedure

1. Set up high-speed oscilloscope with time-calibrated horizontal axis.
2. Switch-on internal sweep.
3. Set SYNC SELECTOR switch to INTERNAL.
4. Set HORIZONTAL and VERTICAL GAIN controls to midrange.
5. Connect equipment as shown in Fig. 4-12A.
6. Set square-wave generator to repetition rate (frequency) of 100 kc.
7. Set R_1 for recommended forward test current, as indicated by milliammeter M.
8. Increase output of generator, noting that pattern appears on screen.
9. Adjust oscilloscope SWEEP FREQUENCY and SYNC controls for a single, stationary pattern.
10. Readjust HORIZONTAL and VERTICAL GAIN controls for suitable height and width.
11. Measure recovery time t (Fig. 4-12B) along time-calibrated horizontal axis. (If dual-trace oscilloscope is used, a timing wave may be displayed simultaneously with main pattern.)
12. Photograph display if permanent record is desired.
13. Repeat test at other square-wave frequencies, if required.

4.11 TRANSISTOR SWITCHING CHARACTERISTICS

Transistors used in digital computers, like diodes, must be capable of fast switching. Figure 4-13A shows a test setup for checking transistor switching characteristics. For this application, a high-speed, dual-trace oscilloscope is required (i.e., one having excellent high-frequency and transient response). The horizontal axis of the instrument must be time calibrated.

In this test, the collector and base of transistor Q are d-c biased, and a 5-μsec 4-v peak pulse is applied to the base-emitter input circuit. This pulse is also applied to the oscilloscope vertical input No. 2. The transistor delivers an output pulse (rotated 180° by the common-emitter circuit) to vertical input No. 1. Figure 4-13B shows the two pulses displayed simultaneously on the screen for easy comparison.

The switching characteristics of the transistor are determined from amplitude and time measurements made on the calibrated vertical and horizontal axes, as indicated in Fig. 4-13B.

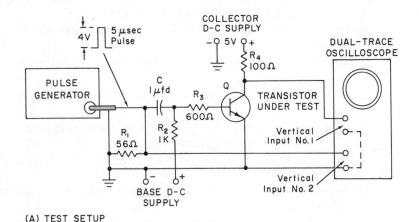

(A) TEST SETUP

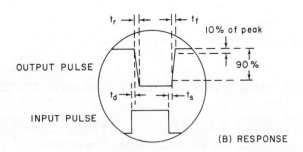

(B) RESPONSE

FIG. 4-13. Transistor switching characteristics.

Test Procedure

1. Set up dual-trace, high-speed oscilloscope having time-calibrated horizontal axis.

2. Switch-on internal recurrent sweep common to both traces.

3. Set SYNC SELECTOR switch to INTERNAL.

4. Set HORIZONTAL and VERTICAL GAIN controls to mid-range (or to calibration point).

5. Connect equipment as shown in Fig. 4-13A.

6. Apply d-c voltages to transistor circuit. (Collector supply voltage is shown as 5 v. Use other value if specified by transistor manufacturer.)

7. Set pulse generator output to 4-v peak (5-μsec pulse width).

8. Adjust oscilloscope SWEEP FREQUENCY and SYNC controls for single, stationary input and output pulses on screen (Fig. 4-13B).

9. Readjust HORIZONTAL and VERTICAL GAIN controls, if necessary.

10. Along time-calibrated horizontal axis, measure delay time t_d, rise time t_r, storage time t_s, and fall time t_f, as indicated in Fig. 4-13B.

11. Compare with transistor manufacturer's switching specifications.

12. Photograph display if permanent record is desired.

13. Repeat test at selected values of applied d-c base voltage.

4.12 TUNNEL DIODE, VISUAL TEST

The negative-resistance curve of a tunnel diode may be displayed by a d-c oscilloscope in the test setup shown in Fig. 4-14A. Both the horizontal and vertical axes must be voltage-calibrated, with the spot positioned at the lower left side of the screen for zero. The oscilloscope must have identical horizontal and vertical channels to eliminate phase difference.

In this arrangement, the tunnel diode (D_2) under test is forward-biased with positive half-cycles of voltage supplied by the IN645 silicon rectifier D_1. The peak voltage, as read on the horizontal axis of the oscilloscope, is adjusted by means of the Variac and must not exceed the maximum recommended d-c forward voltage of the tunnel diode. This voltage is also applied as the sweep voltage to the horizontal input. Tunnel diode current develops a proportional voltage drop across load resistor R_3, and this voltage is applied to the vertical input as a current signal. The result is the forward conduction curve of the tunnel diode with its negative-resistance region, as shown in Fig. 4-14B. Forward voltage is read along the calibrated horizontal axis. Since $R_3 = 10$ ohms, forward current may be determined from the voltage e_f read along the vertical axis by dividing by 10: $I = e_f/10$.

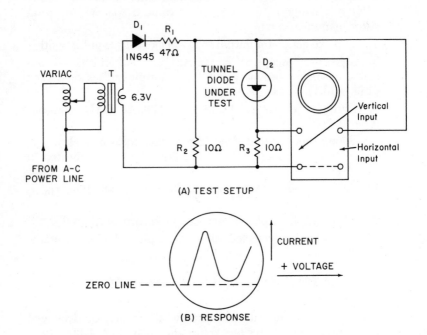

(A) TEST SETUP

(B) RESPONSE

FIG. 4-14. Tunnel diode test.

Test Procedure

1. Set up d-c oscilloscope voltage-calibrated as explained above.

2. Switch-off internal sweep.

3. Set SYNC SELECTOR switch to EXTERNAL.

4. Set HORIZONTAL and VERTICAL GAIN controls to midrange (or to voltage calibration point).

5. Connect equipment as shown in Fig. 4-14A.

6. With tunnel diode (D_2) in circuit, adjust Variac for voltage (as read at right end of pattern on screen) equal to maximum forward voltage recommended by tunnel diode manufacturer (read along horizontal axis).

7. Readjust HORIZONTAL and VERTICAL GAIN controls, if necessary.

8. Read voltage and current (current = 1/10 of vertical voltage) at any point of interest on curve.

9. Photograph display if permanent record is needed.

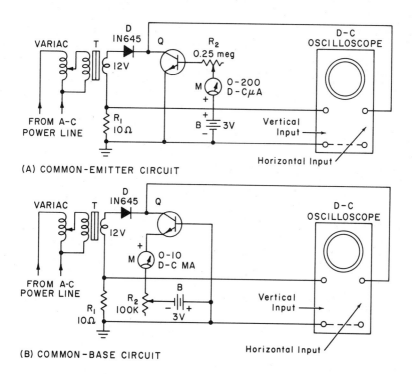

(A) COMMON-EMITTER CIRCUIT

(B) COMMON-BASE CIRCUIT

FIG. 4-15. Transistor test.

4.13 TRANSISTOR, VISUAL TEST

Figure 4-15 shows test setups for instant presentation of the collector voltage—collector current ($v_c i_c$) curve of a transistor. Figure 4-15A gives the circuit for a common-emitter transistor connection; Figure 4-15B gives the circuit for a common-base connection.

In these circuits, the collector voltage consists of positive half-cycles of voltage supplied by silicon rectifier D. This voltage is also presented to the oscilloscope horizontal input for sweep. Collector current flow develops a voltage drop across resistor R_1, and this voltage is applied to the vertical input as the current signal. The transistor d-c base current in Fig. 4-15A or the d-c emitter current in Fig. 4-15B (derived from battery B) is set to the desired test level by means of rheostat R_2 and microammeter or milliammeter M.

A d-c oscilloscope is required. This instrument must have identical horizontal and vertical channels to eliminate phase difference. The horizontal and vertical channels must be d-c voltage-calibrated, with the spot positioned for zero at the left side of the screen.

The $v_c i_c$ curve resembles Fig. 4-16A for the common-emitter, or Fig. 4-16B for the common-base.

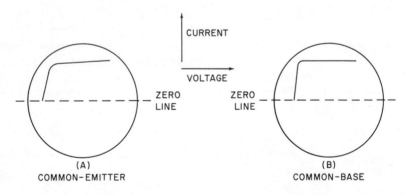

FIG. 4-16. Transistor response patterns.

Test Procedure

1. Set up oscilloscope that has been dc-calibrated as explained above.

2. Switch-off internal sweep.

3. Set SYNC SELECTOR switch to EXTERNAL.

4. Set HORIZONTAL and VERTICAL GAIN controls to mid-range or to calibration point.

5. Set up equipment as shown in Fig. 4-15 (A or B, whichever applies).

6. Adjust Variac to give collector voltage, as read on calibrated horizontal scale, not in excess of rated collector voltage of transistor (Q) under test.

7. Adjust rheostat R_2 for desired base current (Fig. 4-15A) or emitter current (Fig. 4-15B).

8. Observe curve on screen.

9. Read collector voltage (horizontal axis) and collector current (vertical axis) at any point of interest. Since $R_1 = 10$ ohms, current values may be determined by dividing vertical voltage by 10.

10. Repeat test at each desired value of base current or emitter current, and collector voltage.

11. Photograph display if permanent record is needed.

The connections shown in Figs. 4-15A and B are for n-p-n transistors. For p-n-p transistors, reverse polarity of rectifier D, battery B, and meter M. Also, set zero at the right end of the screen (the curves will be the reverse of those shown in Fig. 4-16).

Where this test gives a single curve, more complicated circuits will display an entire family of curves (one for each selected value of base current or emitter current). The equipment for this multiple display is complicated and is available as a specialized oscilloscope (e. g., Tektronix Type 575 Transistor-Curve Tracer). Similar oscilloscopes are also commercially available for presentation of tube curves, such as a family showing plate voltage/plate current vs. grid voltage (e. g., Tektronix Type 570 Electron-Tube Curve-Tracer).

4.14 OSCILLOSCOPE AS BRIDGE NULL DETECTOR

As the null detector for an a-c bridge, the oscilloscope, unlike a meter used for the purpose, gives separate indications for reactive balance and resistive balance of the bridge. Figure 4-17 shows how an oscilloscope is connected to the bridge. Here, T is a shielded transformer, and capacitor C and potentiometer R form an adjustable phase-shift network. The generator voltage is applied simultaneously to the oscilloscope horizontal input (through the phase shifter) and to the bridge input. The bridge output signal is applied to the oscilloscope vertical input. Figure 4-18 shows the type of patterns obtained.

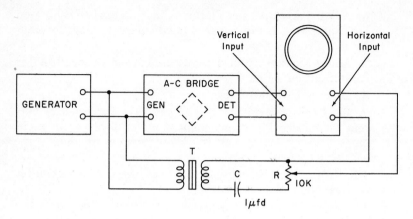

FIG. 4-17. The oscilloscope as a null detector.

Test Procedure

1. Set up oscilloscope.

2. Switch-off internal sweep.

3. Set SYNC SELECTOR switch to EXTERNAL.

4. Set HORIZONTAL and VERTICAL GAIN controls to mid-range.

5. Connect equipment as shown in Fig. 4-17.

6. With bridge unbalanced but with test component (resistor, capacitor, inductor) connected to bridge UNKNOWN terminals, adjust R in phase shifter to give ellipse pattern on screen.

7. Readjust HORIZONTAL and VERTICAL GAIN controls for ellipse of suitable size.

8. Adjust reactance control of bridge, noting that ellipse tilts to right (Fig. 4-18A) or to left (Fig. 4-18C). When reactance balance is complete (reactance null), ellipse will be horizontal (Fig. 4-18B).

9. Adjust resistance (power factor, dissipation factor, or Q) control of bridge, noting that ellipse closes.

10. At complete null (reactance and resistance both balanced), straight horizontal line is obtained (Fig. 4-18E). If resistance is balanced while reactance is unbalanced, tilted ellipse will close, giving single-line trace tilted to the right (Fig. 4-18D) or to the left (Fig. 4-18F).

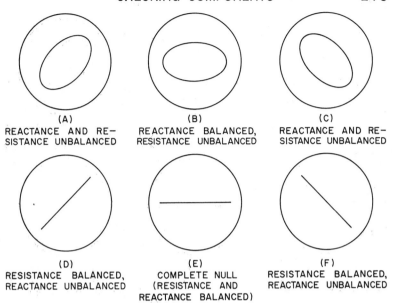

FIG. 4-18. Null detector patterns.

A simpler but less effective way to use an oscilloscope as a null detector is to connect the bridge output (DETECTOR terminals) to the vertical input and use the oscilloscope as a voltmeter which gives its lowest reading at null. This method may be used with internal sweep either on or off. (See *Direct Measurement of Voltage*, Section 5.2, Volume 1.) If a sensitive d-c oscilloscope is used, this method is suitable for d-c, as well as a-c, bridges.

Chapter 5

Performance Checking

The performance of electric and electronic circuits of many kinds (and of some nonelectric circuits as well) may be studied with the oscilloscope. In some applications, this instrument, in effect, plots a performance curve which it presents instantly. In others, it shows wave shape, phase, time, and similar factors. Any nonelectrical phenomenon which can be converted to voltage by means of a transducer may be applied to the oscilloscope for performance testing.

Many tests of electrical and electronic equipment are described in Volume 1. Those explained in this chapter, however, are of a more scientific or industrial nature. Some of the tests of physical quantities in Chapter 3 of this volume may be regarded as performance tests, as well, and may be so applied (overlap in these areas is unavoidable).

The merits of the modern high-performance oscilloscope coupled with the convenience of photographic recording enables laboratory and field testing of equipment otherwise possible only through long, laborious data taking.

5.1 COMMUTATOR RIPPLE IN GENERATORS

The amplitude, frequency, and waveform of ripple in the output of a d-c generator may be checked with the test setup shown in Fig. 5-1A. An a-c oscilloscope is usually used to block the mean d-c output voltage of the generator from the instrument (this voltage is high, compared to that of the ripple and can cause off-screen deflection), and internal recurrent sweep is operated. The ripple-voltage pattern resembles Fig. 5-1B1. The test is made under conditions of no load (switch S open) and full load (switch S closed).

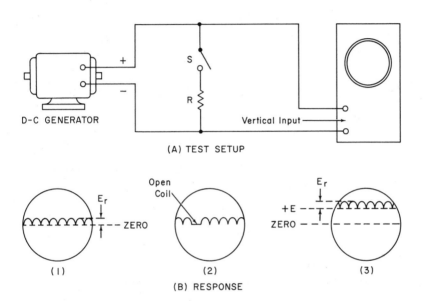

(A) TEST SETUP

(B) RESPONSE

FIG. 5-1. Commutator ripple.

Test Procedure

1. Set up voltage-calibrated a-c oscilloscope.

2. Switch-on internal sweep.

3. Set SYNC SELECTOR switch to INTERNAL.

4. Set HORIZONTAL and VERTICAL GAIN controls to midrange.

5. Connect equipment as shown in Fig. 5-1A—Select resistance R for full load of the generator. Generator output (d-c voltage plus peak ripple voltage) must not exceed maximum safe input voltage rating of oscilloscope.

6. Operate generator, noting that pattern appears on screen.

7. Adjust SWEEP FREQUENCY and SYNC controls for several stationary ripple humps (Fig. 5-1B1).

8. Readjust HORIZONTAL and VERTICAL GAIN controls, if necessary, for suitable width and height of pattern.

9. From voltage-calibrated vertical axis, measure peak amplitude of ripple voltage (E_r in Fig. 5-1B1). Make separate measurements with switch S open and closed.

10. Determine ripple frequency by (a) adjusting SWEEP FREQUENCY and SYNC controls for a single, stationary ripple hump on screen, and (b) reading frequency from calibrated sweep. If oscilloscope does not have frequency-calibrated sweep, use an external audio oscillator (connected to horizontal input) and Lissajous figures to measure frequency.

If a generator armature coil is open, the corresponding ripple hump will be missing from the pattern (Fig. 5-1B2). If one coil has high resistance (loose connection, dirty commutator bar, etc.), the corresponding hump will be lower than the others. Intermittent contact (brush chatter) will produce fluctuations and noise waves on the ripple trace.

Sometimes it is desired to observe both output voltage and ripple simultaneously. This is a composite-voltage measurement and requires a d-c oscilloscope. The d-c output deflects the base line upward from zero to $+E$ (equal to the output voltage), as shown in Fig. 5-1B3. Ripple voltage E_r is then measured from the $+E$ line to the peaks of the humps. However, low ripple is difficult to measure when $+E$ is very high compared to E_r.

5.2 POWER SUPPLY RIPPLE

Ripple in the d-c output of an ac-operated power supply (including the vibrator type and electronic inverter type) is due to the a-c supply. Its amplitude and frequency depend upon whether the rectifier circuit is half-wave or full-wave and whether the a-c supply is single-phase or polyphase. Measurement is similar to that of commutator ripple (described in Section 5.1).

Figure 5-2A shows the test setup. An a-c oscilloscope is used to block the mean d-c output voltage of the power supply from the oscilloscope (this voltage is high, compared to the ripple, and can cause off-screen deflection), and the internal recurrent sweep is operated. The ripple-voltage pattern resembles Fig. 5-2B1 for full-wave rectification, and Fig. 5-2B2 for half-wave rectification. These wave shapes apply both to single-phase and polyphase operation. The test is made under conditions of no load (switch S open) and full load (switch S closed).

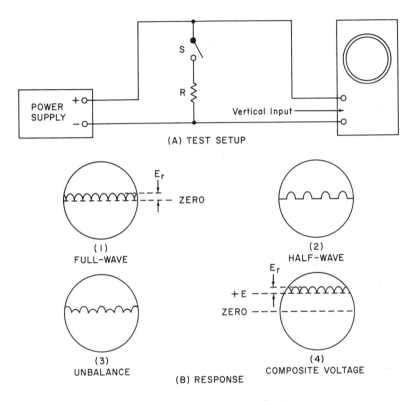

FIG. 5-2. Power supply ripple.

Test Procedure

1. Set up voltage-calibrated a-c oscilloscope.

2. Switch-on internal sweep.

3. Set SYNC SELECTOR switch to INTERNAL.

4. Set HORIZONTAL and VERTICAL GAIN controls to mid-range.

5. Connect equipment as shown in Fig. 5-2A—Select resistance R for full load of power supply. Power supply output (d-c voltage plus peak ripple voltage) must not exceed maximum safe input voltage rating of oscilloscope.

6. Switch-on power supply, noting that pattern appears on screen.

7. Adjust SWEEP FREQUENCY and SYNC controls for several, stationary ripple humps (Fig. 5-2B1 for full-wave supply; Fig. 5-2B2 for half-wave supply).

8. Readjust HORIZONTAL and VERTICAL GAIN controls, if necessary, for suitable width and height of pattern.

9. From voltage-calibrated vertical axis, measure peak amplitude of ripple voltage (see E_r in Fig. 5-2B1). Make separate measurements with switch S open and closed.

10. Determine ripple frequency by (a) adjusting SWEEP FREQUENCY and SYNC controls for a single, stationary ripple hump on screen, and (b) reading frequency from calibrated sweep. If oscilloscope does not have frequency-calibrated sweep, use an external audio oscillator (connected to horizontal input) and Lissajous figures to measure frequency.

If the halves of a full-wave circuit are unbalanced (mismatched rectifiers, one defective rectifier, unequal loading, breakdown on one side, etc.), the humps will alternate in height, as shown in Fig. 5-2B3. If the half-wave pattern (Fig. 5-2B1) is obtained from a full-wave power supply, one-half of the circuit is dead. Electrical noise generated by the power supply will produce fluctuations and noise waves on the ripple trace.

Sometimes, it is desired to observe output voltage and ripple simultaneously. This is a composite voltage measurement and requires a d-c oscilloscope. Circuit connections are the same as in Fig. 5-2A. The d-c output of the power supply deflects the base line upward from zero to $+E$ (equal to the output voltage), as shown in Fig. 5-2B4. Ripple voltage E_r is then measured from the $+E$ line to the peaks of the humps. However, low ripple is difficult to measure when $+E$ is very high compared to E_r.

5.3 MULTIVIBRATOR SIGNAL VOLTAGES

Important characteristics of multivibrator signal voltages are peak amplitude, waveform, duration, and repetition rate. All may be determined from a single oscilloscope display. A calibrated oscilloscope used in this application must have high frequency capability and excellent transient response. It should also be equipped with a low-capacitance probe. Internal recurrent sweep is used.

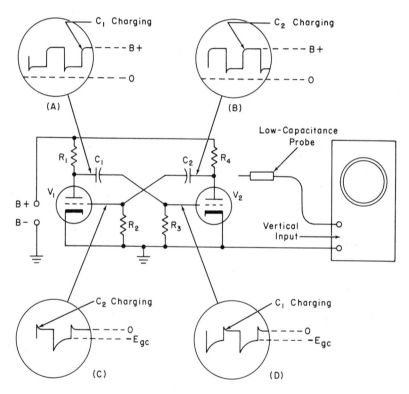

FIG. 5-3. Multivibrator test.

Multivibrators, very useful in modern electronics, are of many types and not all of them can be treated in this limited space. Figure 5-3 shows a typical, symmetrical, free-running multivibrator circuit with grid- and plate-voltage waveforms indicated at (A), (B), (C), and (D). Patterns resembling these are obtained when the low-capacitance probe is touched to the corresponding circuit points.

Test Procedure

1. Set up voltage-calibrated, time-calibrated oscilloscope having low-capacitance probe.

2. Switch-on internal sweep.

3. Set SYNC SELECTOR switch to INTERNAL.

4. Set HORIZONTAL and VERTICAL GAIN controls to mid-range.

5. Connect equipment as shown in Fig. 5-3.

6. Switch-on multivibrator.

7. Touch low-capacitance probe to circuit test point.

8. Adjust SWEEP FREQUENCY and SYNC controls for two or three stationary pulses on screen.

9. Readjust HORIZONTAL and VERTICAL GAIN controls, if necessary, for suitable width and height of pattern.

10. Measure pulse amplitudes of interest on voltage-calibrated vertical axis.

11. Measure pulse times of interest on time-calibrated horizontal axis.

12. Measure pulse repetition rate (multivibrator frequency) by (a) adjusting SWEEP FREQUENCY and SYNC controls for a single, stationary pulse on screen, and (b) reading frequency from sweep controls. If oscilloscope has time-calibrated sweep, calculate frequency from time indication. If oscilloscope has no sweep calibration, use an external oscillator or signal generator (connected to horizontal input) and Lissajous figures to measure frequency.

With a dual-trace oscilloscope, grid and plate waves may be displayed simultaneously for comparison.

5.4 BLOCKING-OSCILLATOR SIGNAL VOLTAGES

The blocking oscillator, like the multivibrator, is widely used in modern electronics. Characteristics of particular interest in blocking-oscillator signal voltages are peak amplitude, waveform, duration, and repetition rate. All of these may be determined from a single display by a calibrated oscilloscope that has high frequency capability and excellent transient response and is equipped with a low-capacitance probe.

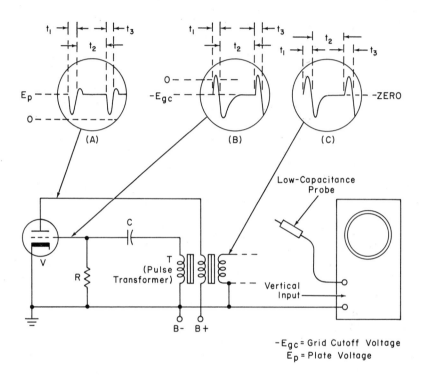

$-E_{gc}$ = Grid Cutoff Voltage
E_p = Plate Voltage

FIG. 5-4. Blocking-oscillator test.

There are many kinds of blocking-oscillator circuits, both tube- and transistor-type. Figure 5-4 shows a typical circuit with plate-, grid-, and output-voltage waves indicated at (A), (B), and (C), respectively. In each of these displays, t_1 and t_3 represent conduction-time intervals, t_2 represents the cutoff-time interval, and E_{gc} represents the grid voltage for plate current cutoff. Patterns resembling these are obtained when the low-capacitance probe is touched to the corresponding circuit points.

Test Procedure

1. Set up voltage-calibrated, time-calibrated oscilloscope having low-capacitance probe.

2. Switch-on internal sweep.

3. Set SYNC SELECTOR switch to INTERNAL.

4. Set HORIZONTAL and VERTICAL GAIN controls to midrange.

5. Connect equipment as shown in Fig. 5-4.

6. Switch-on blocking oscillator.

7. Touch low-capacitance probe to circuit test point.

8. Adjust SWEEP FREQUENCY and SYNC controls for two stationary pulses on screen.

9. Readjust HORIZONTAL and VERTICAL GAIN controls, if necessary, for suitable width and height of pattern.

10. Measure pulse amplitudes of interest on voltage-calibrated vertical axis.

11. Measure pulse times of interest on time-calibrated horizontal axis.

12. Measure pulse repetition rate (oscillator frequency) by (a) adjusting SWEEP FREQUENCY and SYNC controls for a single, stationary pulse on screen, and (b) reading frequency from sweep controls. If oscilloscope has time-calibrated sweep, calculate frequency from time indication. If oscilloscope sweep is uncalibrated, use an external oscillator or signal generator (connected to horizontal input) and Lissajous figures to measure frequency.

13. If repetition rate is too low for a usable stationary display on screen, photograph display for later study and measurement.

With a dual-trace oscilloscope, two waves may be displayed simultaneously for comparison. A multiple-trace instrument will permit display of all three oscillator waves plus a timing wave.

5.5 FILTER RESPONSE

It is well known that the response curve of a radio-frequency tuned circuit or network may be displayed instantly on an oscilloscope screen when the r-f test signal is derived from a sweep signal generator. Points on the curve are identified in frequency by means of a marker generator. This technique is often used in studies of radio and TV receiver passband and is described in Chapter 9 of Volume 1.

It perhaps is not as well known that a similar technique may be used to display the response curve of an audio-frequency network, such as a wave filter. This method is advantageous when a series of adjustments must be made to a filter, and a large number of point-by-point measurements would otherwise have to be made to show the total effect of each adjustment. For this application, an a-f sweep signal generator is required. This may be either an instrument (such as Kay Model M) embodying electronic sweep that can be used with any oscilloscope, or an a-f oscillator or signal generator tuned over its frequency range by means of a synchronous dial drive (such as General Radio Type 908) used with a long-persistence oscilloscope, storage-type oscilloscope, or camera-equipped oscilloscope.

Figure 5-5A shows a fully electronic test setup. In this arrangement, the generator supplies a swept signal (e. g., 20 cps to 20 kc), sweep voltage for the oscilloscope, and markers for identifying frequency points on the displayed curve. The oscilloscope vertical channel must have good frequency response up to at least twice the highest frequency at which the filter is to be tested. Figure 5-5B shows typical response curves for high-pass, low-pass, band-pass, and band-suppression filters.

Test Procedure

1. Set up voltage-calibrated oscilloscope.

2. Switch-off internal sweep.

3. Set SWEEP SELECTOR switch to EXTERNAL.

4. Set SYNC SELECTOR switch to EXTERNAL.

5. Set HORIZONTAL and VERTICAL GAIN controls to mid-range.

6. Connect equipment as shown in Fig. 5-5A—Choose resistance R_s equal to input impedance of filter under test; choose resistance R_p equal to output impedance of filter; connect sweep-generator sweep output to HORIZONTAL INPUT terminal, as shown, unless oscilloscope has separate terminal for external sweep input.

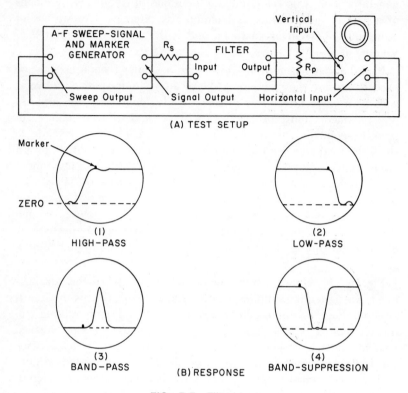

(A) TEST SETUP

(1) HIGH-PASS

(2) LOW-PASS

(3) BAND-PASS

(4) BAND-SUPPRESSION

(B) RESPONSE

FIG. 5-5. Filter test.

7. Set generator sweep width for desired frequency test range (e.g., 50 cps to 20 kc).

8. Adjust generator output amplitude, noting that pattern appears on screen.

9. Readjust HORIZONTAL and VERTICAL GAIN controls, if necessary, for suitable width and height of pattern.

10. Identify frequency points of interest on displayed curve by means of marker (see Fig. 5-5B) delivered by generator, and read frequency from generator marker dial.

11. Measure amplitude of any point of interest on curve by means of voltage-calibrated vertical axis.

5.6 INTERNAL COMBUSTION ENGINE PRESSURE

Dynamic engine pressure under actual operating conditions may be checked with the setup shown in Fig. 5-6A. The pressure pickup is one of the piezoelectric units combined with a spark plug. A typical response curve, as displayed by the oscilloscope, is shown in Fig. 5-6B.

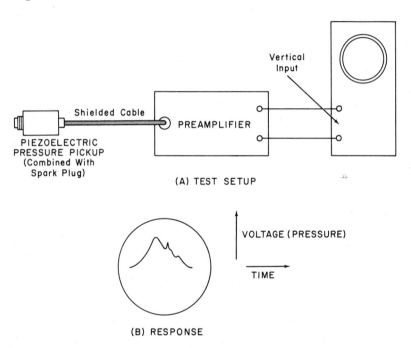

Vertical Input

Shielded Cable

PREAMPLIFIER

PIEZOELECTRIC
PRESSURE PICKUP
(Combined With
Spark Plug)

(A) TEST SETUP

VOLTAGE (PRESSURE)

TIME

(B) RESPONSE

FIG. 5-6. Engine pressure test.

Test Procedure

1. Set up voltage-calibrated, time-calibrated oscilloscope.

2. Switch-on internal sweep.

3. Set SYNC SELECTOR switch to INTERNAL.

4. Set HORIZONTAL and VERTICAL GAIN controls to mid-range.

5. Connect equipment as shown in Fig. 5-6A. The preamplifier must be voltage-calibrated or it must have accurately known single-valued gain, in order that the vertical deflection of the oscilloscope may be read as the actual voltage output of the pressure pickup.

6. Operate engine, noting that pattern similar to Fig. 5-6B appears on screen.

7. Adjust SWEEP FREQUENCY and SYNC controls for single, stationary pressure pulse on screen.

8. Readjust HORIZONTAL and VERTICAL GAIN controls, if necessary, for suitable width and height of pattern.

9. Read voltage amplitude at points of interest on curve. Convert to output voltage of pressure pickup.

10. Convert voltage amplitude to pressure units by reference to calibration figure (psi/v) supplied by manufacturer of pressure pickup.

11. Read time at points of interest on curve by means of time-calibrated horizontal axis. If dual-trace oscilloscope is used, a convenient timing wave may be displayed simultaneously with pressure curve.

12. Repeat test at higher sweep frequency to give several pulses showing any change in pressure during successive engine cycles.

This test method is applicable also to other devices in which pressure is generated, such as guns, pumps, hydraulic and pneumatic pipe lines, expansion chambers, etc.

5.7 THYRATRON CONDUCTION ANGLE

In thyratron tubes used in the control of welders, motors, and other equipment, the phase and/or amplitude of the a-c grid-control signal is adjusted so that anode current is initiated at a selected point on the grid-voltage cycle and continues to flow until the half-cycle of anode voltage reaches zero and cuts it off. This current flow is conveniently described with reference to grid-cycle angle. Thus, anode current (I_a) might start when the grid-voltage positive half-cycle is at $20°$ and continue to flow until this half-cycle falls to zero at $180°$—a $160°$ flow angle.

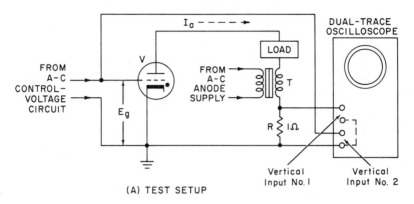

(A) TEST SETUP

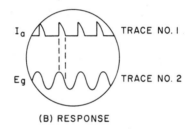

(B) RESPONSE

FIG. 5-7. Thyratron conduction angle.

The thyratron conduction angle may be determined readily from a simultaneous display of grid voltage and anode current by a dual-trace oscilloscope. Figure 5-7 shows a test setup. Here, resistor R is temporarily connected in series with the anode, external load device, and anode supply transformer. The resistance is kept low (e.g., 1 ohm) so that its presence does not degrade circuit operation. Anode current flowing through this resistor develops a voltage drop which is applied to one vertical input. The grid voltage is applied to the other vertical input. Figure 5-7B shows the type of display obtained. In this example, Trace 1 depicts anode current and Trace 2 depicts grid voltage. Note that here anode current starts to flow when grid voltage is at 90° and continues to flow until grid voltage reaches 180°—a 90° conduction angle.

Test Procedure

1. Set up dual-trace oscilloscope.

2. Switch-on internal sweep, common to both traces.

3. Set SYNC SELECTOR switch to INTERNAL.

4. Set HORIZONTAL and VERTICAL GAIN controls to mid-range.

5. Connect equipment as shown in Fig. 5-7A.

6. Switch-on thyratron circuit and adjust it as required, noting that pattern appears on screen.

7. Adjust SWEEP FREQUENCY and SYNC controls for two or three stationary cycles of each wave on screen.

8. Readjust HORIZONTAL and VERTICAL GAIN controls, if necessary, for suitable width and height of pattern.

9. On the basis of 1 uncontrolled conduction pulse $= 180°$, determine by reference to the grid-voltage wave (Trace 2) the angle of flow of anode current, as depicted by any of the conduction pulses (Fig. 5-7B).

5.8 CAMERA SHUTTER SPEED

The speed of operation of a camera shutter or similar light gate may be measured with the test setup shown in Fig. 5-8A. An oscilloscope having a time-calibrated horizontal axis is required.

In the test setup, a dc-operated lamp is mounted rigidly in front of the camera (alternating current will produce fluctuations in light and this will wrinkle the test pattern). A tiny 1N77B germanium photodiode is placed inside the camera and pointed toward the lens. While the shutter is open, the illuminated photodiode conducts current from battery B through resistor R. When the shutter is closed, the cell is darkened and the current ceases. The short burst of current produced by the rapid opening and closing of the shutter produces a voltage drop of short duration across resistor R, and this voltage is presented to the vertical input of the oscilloscope to produce a pulse on the screen (see Fig. 5-8B). The width of the top of this pulse (t in Fig. 5-8B) is proportional to the open-time of the shutter, and the time interval is determined from the time-calibrated horizontal axis. Because shutters are rapid in action, the pulse will not remain long on the screen of a conventional oscilloscope. Therefore, the pattern must be photographed or a storage-type oscilloscope used.

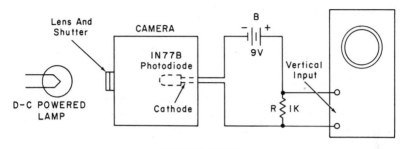

(A) TEST SETUP

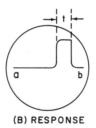

(B) RESPONSE

FIG. 5-8. Camera shutter speed.

Test Procedure

1. Set up time-calibrated oscilloscope. Instrument must be either camera-equipped or of the storage type.

2. Switch-on internal recurrent sweep.

3. Set SYNC SELECTOR switch to INTERNAL.

4. Set HORIZONTAL and VERTICAL GAIN controls to mid-range.

5. Connect equipment as shown in Fig. 5-8A, turn on lamp, and close shutter of camera under test.

6. Set HORIZONTAL GAIN control to confine horizontal trace inside screen (from a to b in Fig. 5-8B). If this is not done, image may fall off screen.

7. Make test run: (a) Operate shutter; (b) observe quick pulse on screen; and (c) readjust VERTICAL GAIN control, if necessary, for suitable pulse height.

8. Attach oscilloscope camera.

9. Hold shutter of oscilloscope camera open (bulb position), operate shutter of camera under test, and develop picture.

10. Along time-calibrated horizontal axis on picture, determine time interval (t) during which shutter of test camera was open.

If a dual-trace oscilloscope is used, a timing wave may be displayed simultaneously with the test pulse for easy comparison. If the oscilloscope has no time calibration, determine time interval t in the following manner:

1. Without disturbing any of the oscilloscope control settings, remove test circuit and in its place connect a variable-frequency oscillator to the VERTICAL INPUT terminals.

2. Tune the oscillator to obtain a single, stationary cycle which exactly fills the space from a to b (Fig. 5-8B).

3. Read frequency f from the oscillator dial.

4. Determine time interval between a and b: $T_1 = 1/f$, where T_1 is in seconds, and f in cps.

5. Calculate shutter time: $T_2 = T_1(D_2/D_1)$, where T_1 and T_2 are in seconds, D_1 is the distance (in screen divisions) between a and b, and D_2 is the width of the pulse (in screen divisions).

5.9 ROLE OF OSCILLOSCOPE IN COMPUTER TESTING

The oscilloscope has three main functions in computer work: circuit testing, computer readout, and troubleshooting. It is used with analog and digital computers. In each case, the utility of this instrument results from its high input impedance (negligible loading of the computer circuit) and its ability to display pulse shape and changes, as well as signal amplitude. With a multiple-trace oscilloscope, separate information can be displayed simultaneously (e.g., clock pulses together with adder output pulses in a digital computer, or input and output waves in an analog computer).

Because of the high speed of the digital computer, an oscilloscope used with that machine must have a wide vertical passband and excellent transient response, and it must be equipped with a low-capacitance probe. Generally, a passband extending from dc to 200 kc is adequate for analog computer applications, but here again, excellent transient response is required because some dynamic data may embody rapid changes.

The signals in the digital computer are fast pulses related to each other in various ways. The signals in the analog computer may be voltage amplitudes, pulses, or curves which depict variation of some function. The operator must know exactly what kind of signal should appear at each point in either of these circuits in order to interpret profitably the oscilloscope pattern either in troubleshooting or readout. Because analog and digital computers may be used in numerous ways to handle data of various sorts, not every situation can be treated in this volume. Illustrative applications are presented.

Much of computer troubleshooting consists of testing familiar individual quantities, components, or circuits. Many of these tests are detailed elsewhere (see Sections 3.1, 3.2, 3.4, 3.6, 3.7, 4.1, 4.2, 4.9, 4.10, 4.13, 5.3, and 5.4). However, much of it also demands solid knowledge of computer theory and operation. In this connection, the reader is referred to the following Rider books: *Basic Pulses,* Irving Gottlieb; *Basics of Analog Computers,* T. D. Truitt and A. E. Rogers; *Basics of Digital Computers* (3 volumes), John S. Murphy; and *Understanding Digital Computers,* Ronald Benrey.

Signal Amplitude in Analog Computer. Measure signal-voltage amplitude, using either of the standard methods for voltage measurement (Volume 1, Chapter 5). Use a-c or d-c oscilloscope as required. When voltage is alternating, fluctuating, or pulsating, frequency and transient characteristics of the oscilloscope must be adequate for faithful reproduction of the shapes.

Operational amplifiers in analog computers may be set up in various ways with resistance (R) and capacitance (C) to handle calculations with a varying input signal (E_i). For example, a differentiating amplifier will give an output voltage:

$$E_o = (dE_i/dt)RC,$$

and an integrating amplifier will give:

$$E_o = (1/RC) \int_{t1}^{t2} E_i \ dt.$$

Output voltage of the differentiating amplifier is proportional to rate of change (dE_i/dt) of input voltage E_i; output voltage of the integrating amplifier evaluates the area under the E_i curve. Thus, these are calculating amplifiers. The values of E_i, E_o, t_1 and t_2 are measured on the voltage-calibrated vertical axis and time-calibrated horizontal axis, respectively.

Nonrepetitive data will not give a stationary display on the screen unless a storage-type oscilloscope is used. When this type of instrument is not available, photograph the display for later study and measurement.

Current Component in Analog Computer. Current can be measured by the inserted-resistor method (Sections 5.6 and 5.7, Volume 1), but the current-probe method (Section 3.1, Volume 2) should be used wherever insertion of a resistor might degrade circuit operation. Current components are handled in calculations in much the same way that voltage components are used in the preceding explanation.

Gain of Operational Amplifier in Analog Computer. Measure operational-amplifier voltage gain (a-c or d-c) by the conventional method of separately determining input voltage E_i and output voltage E_o and calculating:

$$VG = E_o/E_i.$$

The test signal may be supplied by the data signal entering the amplifier from the rest of the computer system, or by an a-c or d-c source (whichever applies). Measure the gain under open-loop conditions, unless instructed otherwise.

Dual Presentation of Analog Computer Information. With a dual-trace oscilloscope, two signals (such as input and output information of an operational amplifier) may be displayed simultaneously for comparison. This is a convenience in some calculations. The number of signals which may be handled simultaneously may be further increased by using a multiple-trace oscilloscope.

Checking Clock Signal in Digital Computer. For this test, connect the oscilloscope vertical input to the clock generator output (often this is the clock track output of a revolving memory drum) and adjust the sweep frequency and internal sync for one stationary pulse on the screen. Check amplitude, duration, rise time, fall time, and overshoot of pulse (see Section 3.4). Determine the pulse repetition rate (clock frequency) from calibrated sweep controls: it is that sweep frequency which produces one pulse on the screen. Also observe if the pulse is free of vertical and horizontal jitter (vibration), and check for noise in the clock output (Section 3.7).

Inverter Operation in Digital Computer. A properly operating inverter stage will flip an applied pulse over. This action results from the 180° phase shift introduced by the stage.

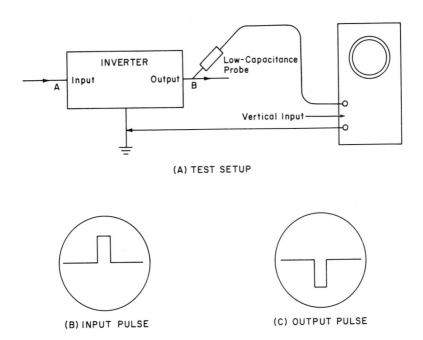

(A) TEST SETUP

(B) INPUT PULSE   (C) OUTPUT PULSE

FIG. 5-9. Inverter operation.

The oscilloscope may be used, as shown in Fig. 5-9A, to check inverter operation. The input signal of the stage is supplied by a pulse generator, and the oscilloscope sweep and internal sync are adjusted for a single, stationary pulse on the screen (a signal pulse in the computer also may be used). When the low-capacitance probe is touched to input point A, an upright pulse (Fig. 5-9B) is obtained; when the probe is touched to output point B, an upside-down pulse (Fig. 5-9C) is obtained if the inverter is operating correctly.

The patterns shown in Fig. 5-9B and C result from a positive (or positive-going) input pulse. If a negative input pulse is used, Fig. 5-9B will be upside-down instead, and Fig. 5-9C will be upright, to indicate correct operation.

The output pulse should be examined for evidence of any amplitude or time distortion introduced by the inverter.

Digital Memory Output. The contents of an operating memory unit in a digital computer may be sampled with the oscilloscope vertical input connected to the memory output. The oscilloscope sync must be internal, and the sweep set to a frequency low enough (compared to the computer clock frequency) to display as many memory pulses as can be read on the screen.

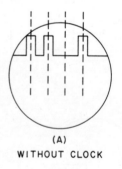

(A)
WITHOUT CLOCK

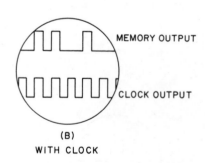

MEMORY OUTPUT

CLOCK OUTPUT

(B)
WITH CLOCK

FIG. 5-10. Memory output.

Figure 5-10A shows the type of display obtained. Here, the dotted vertical lines correspond to the clock pulse positions. The solid line trace shows pulses "read out" of the memory and, in this illustration, corresponds to 1101 which is the binary form of the number *thirteen*.

If a dual-trace oscilloscope is used, the clock pulses may be displayed simultaneously with the memory pulses, as shown in Fig. 5-10B. Here, the second vertical input is connected to the clock output.

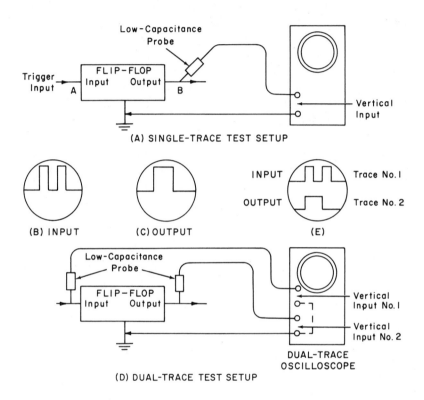

FIG. 5-11. Flip-flop operation.

Digital Computer Flip-Flop Operation. Flip-flops are employed in large numbers in a digital computer. Since these units are bistable, they are essentially scale-of-two counters. Several types are used in digital systems—tube, transistor, tunnel diode, magnetic, and electrostatic. Flip-flop operation may be checked with the test setup shown in Fig. 5-11A. In this arrangement, the low-capacitance probe is touched first to input point A of the operating flip-flop, and the oscilloscope sweep frequency and internal sync are adjusted for two, stationary input-trigger pulses on the screen (Fig. 5-11B). Without disturbing the settings of the oscilloscope controls, the probe is then transferred to flip-flop output point B. The image at this point will be a single output pulse (Fig. 5-11C) since a correctly operating flip-flop will halve the input-trigger frequency (repetition rate).

A dual-trace oscilloscope may be connected to the flip-flop as shown in Fig. 5-11D. The corresponding output pattern (Trace 2) and input pattern (Trace 1) are shown in Fig. 5-11E.

Digital Computer Logic-Circuit Elements. Operation of the basic AND and OR logic elements may be checked by observing the coincidence and noncoincidence of input and output pulses associated with these elements. Although the position of the pulses may be determined separately along the time-calibrated horizontal axis of a single-trace oscilloscope, accuracy is improved by observing the pulses simultaneously with a multi-trace instrument.

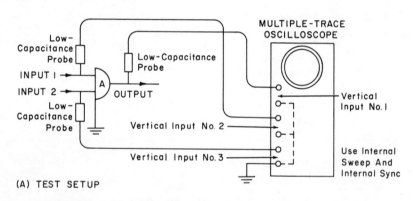

(A) TEST SETUP

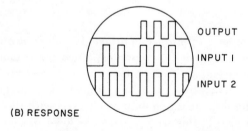

(B) RESPONSE

FIG. 5-12. AND circuit check.

Figure 5-12A shows a test setup for the AND element. As shown in Fig. 5-12B, this logic element, when operating correctly produces an output pulse only when input 1 and input 2 both receive input pulses simultaneously.

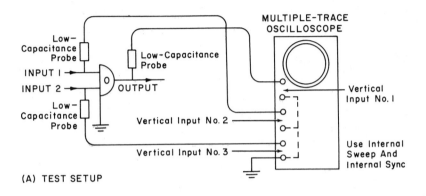

(A) TEST SETUP

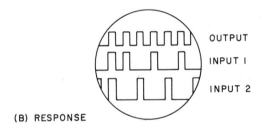

(B) RESPONSE

FIG. 5-13. OR circuit check.

Figure 5-13A shows a test setup for the OR element. As shown in Fig. 5-13B, this logic element, when operating correctly, produces an output pulse when either input receives a pulse.

Elaborations of these circuits, or combinations of AND and OR circuits may be checked in a similar fashion. Thus, a matrix may be considered to be a number of specially connected AND circuits so arranged that an output pulse occurs at a given terminal only when a certain combination of input terminals receive pulses.

INDEX